John Taylor

www.smokeburns.com

The author of this work is identified as John Taylor.

Illustrations copyright © 2007 Taylor Made Solutions (York) Ltd designed by John Taylor and drawn by John Barclay and Neil Stephenson

Photographs courtesy of Fire Instructors Training Products Ltd - www.fitp-ltd.com
and the private collections of John Taylor, Jim Mastin and Ian Roberts.

Edited by, Mavis Garratt and Joseph William Taylor.

A CIP catalogue record for this title is available from the British Library
ISBN 978-1-904446-09-5

Conditions of Sale

Printed and bound in Great Britain
by Quacks Ltd, York, England

Disclaimer

This work analyses and sets out procedures for identifying and dealing with a number of particularly dangerous and difficult situations which arise in the course of dealing with fires occurring inside enclosed structures. The adoption and successful implementation of any particular procedure depends critically upon the correct identification of the situation in which it is to be executed. The advice given in this book is intended solely for professional fire-fighters who have been trained in and have experience of fire fighting in and around such structures. Before attempting to implement any of the procedures described in this book a fire-fighter must satisfy him/herself that he/she has the necessary knowledge and expertise to correctly identify the particular risk with which he/she is or may be dealing and that he/she understands fully the procedure to be adopted. None of the procedures described in this book should be adopted unless they have first been practised in a controlled simulation situation with the appropriate back up support and assistance. Save where it is not, as a matter of law, permissible to exclude such liability for any loss or damage of whatever kind which may be alleged to have been caused, either directly or indirectly, by any claimed reliance on any advice given in this book or as a result of any alleged failure to advise or other omission in material set out herein.

The Publishers - Taylor Made Solutions (York) Ltd, Registered Company No. 4947420 (England & Wales), trade and are governed and construed in accordance with the laws of England and Wales whose courts shall be courts of competent jurisdiction.

Dedication

This book is dedicated to all the fallen fire-fighters and their families, throughout the world and the ages.

To make sense of their tragic loss;

"May their bravery and courage be our guiding light to safety".

John Taylor.
20 May 1999

And

In memory of two wonderful people (Bill & Cath Taylor) who sacrificed all they could to make sure I got an education, without which I would not have had the privilege of attending Xaverian College, Manchester, where some marvellous teachers taught me;

'Some men see the world as it is and ask, "Why?"
Others dream of things that have never been and ask, "Why Not?"

Contents

Chapter 5
Cold Smoke Conditions

Chapter 6

Chapter 7
Standard Operating Procedures (SOPs)
Search and Rescue

Part One – Hot Smoke Conditions

Part Two - The Final Frontier

Part Three – Cold Smoke Conditions

Chapter 8

FOREWORD

Just when I thought I had studied enough about fire and how to put it out, I met John at a conference and listened to his four hour lecture. I soon realized that although my study in Fire Science and research work has led me to create a great tool that uses water mist to fight fire, this tool needed a tactic to go along with it in order for it to be a complete service "product". In "Smoke Burns", John has effectively developed a new tactic to fight fires, one, which I predict will become part of standard operating procedures (SOPs) in the near future. Any fire-fighters or fire officers who read this book will learn not only how to protect themselves better, but also the society they serve as well. John wrote this book wishing that every fire-fighter goes home safely after the job. His love of the fire service and his love for people are sincere as only a person with a great love to this world would dedicate so much of his time to share his book with the public.

Our world has been dramatically changed by "global warming". This results in more fires in the future, and less water to fight it with. This, in turn, makes a fire-fighter's job much tougher. As our resources change, so must our standard operating procedures (SOPs). During my career, I have joined the fire department with more of a fire engineering background than fire-fighting background. I worried for the future of fire-fighting but used my strengths in engineering to view the problem. I was not able to come up with a perfect solution, until I met John and read this book. Now I know I will work with John to continue testing and training based on his theory, and hopefully, I can make a contribution to John's theory and tactics. I admire John's hard work in research and development, and especially, his strength and perseverance to complete this book. To me, John's passion is very evident and I want to thank him for this book.

I know there are many people who are much more qualified than me to write this foreword for John. It really put me on the spot because I am not a native-born American and to use English to express my appreciation of his work was difficult for me because there are just not enough words that can help me express how great this book truly is. I can only give my true feelings and hope that my mediocre writing skills are enough to convey the passion with which the book was written. If you are a responsible fire officer, fire-fighter, spouse or parent, you have to read this book and think about it, use it, and go home safely every day after the job is done. In science, we always say that, "The truth is the truth". What John has written in this book is all truth, which has been neglected by us for a long time.

Ping-Li Yen.
May 28, 2007.

Ping-Li Yen

Since 2000, Ping has been the Fire Protection Research & Development Chief/CEO – CAFS UNIT, Inc. Responsible for all Fire Suppression and Fire Protection Technology Research and Development, including design and build of a special application small and midsize compressed air foam system (CAFS) fire engine, currently being tested and used in Asian countries and development of three water mist systems with international patents obtained and one is currently approved by Factory Mutual Risk Management.

Ping has also been a Fire Prevention Instructor for the California State Fire Marshal's Office since 1998 and co-ordinates Search and Rescue Training classes for Taiwan Red Cross, Taipei Fire Department and Taiwan NFA and began teaching at the National Fire Academy, Emmitsburg, Maryland, United States of America (USA) in 2006.

Ping has also performed the following roles:

Senior Fire Inspector/Fire Investigator/Deputy Fire Marshal –
The City of Arcadia Fire Department (1996-2000).
Fire Prevention Specialist – The City of Pasadena Fire Department (1993-96).
Fire Protection Chief Engineer/Vice President –
Fountain Fire Protection, Inc (1985-1993).
Public Work Department Assistant Engineer –
The City of Beverly Hills (1982-85).

His inventions and patents include:

Commercial Oil Cooker Water Mist System 2000
Portable Water Mist Fire Extinguisher Rated 2A, B, C, K 2001
Industrial Oil Cooker Water Mist System (FM approved 08/26/05)
Small Fire-fighting Vehicle and Trailers utilizing CAFS and Water Mist 2001

John Taylor

Author's Notes

This book is a reflection on my 26 years as a serving fire-fighter and fire officer.

My observations are exactly what I've seen, whilst fire-fighting in real fires and my explanations are purposefully aimed at educating and informing fire-fighters and members of the public, alike, by trying to describe in simplistic terms the 'mechanism of fire' and how and why 'smoke burns'.

I have been taught fire-fighting by the some of the best fire-fighters in the world and most of the techniques advocated by the standard operating procedures (SOPs) in this book are a culmination of the good practices handed down by generations of fire-fighters, worldwide, who have instinctively known of the inherent dangers of flashovers and backdrafts and acted accordingly, but we've always had chinks in our armour and blind spots, which has sadly resulted in the line of duty deaths (LODD) of fire-fighters, whilst dealing with the devastating effects of flashovers and backdrafts. The main purpose of this book is to provide fire-fighters with information on how to enhance existing SOPs by acquiring additional knowledge, training and equipment to make them completely integral and safe on the fire-ground, ensuring that they too, return home safe to their families after every fire they attend.

PROLOGUE

'Smoke Burns'

"If what you see conflicts with what you read – believe what you see".
William. E. Clark. 25 March 1995.

The late Bill Clark kindly came to the first ever International Practical Flashover Training Conference, facilitated by the Yorkshire & Humberside Branch of the Institution of the Fire Engineers (IFE) at West Yorkshire Fire Service Training Centre, Birkenshaw, on 25 March 1995 as a guest speaker. His presentation was one of the most interesting and well received of the day. Bill was 84 years of age at the time and had been involved in trying to understand fire development his entire long and meritorious career, which included serving in the City of New York Fire Department (FDNY).

His knowledge and understanding of the subject and wisdom imparted to myself is one of the most treasured memories of my journey into the world of fire development. The good humour and intelligent approach was wonderful to behold and we all owe Bill a great debt of gratitude for his pioneering work. I was fortunate enough to meet one of his best friends a year later in 1996 – Jon Haguland at the Maryland Fire and Rescue Institute (MFRI), United States of America (USA). I'd just finished a presentation and was leaving the auditorium when this arm placed itself around my shoulder and it was like an old friend had embraced me and then, a feeling of warmth passed through me.

This voice said, "Don't worry about the doubters, John, of which there will be many. You are on the right track my son. Keep going and finish off the work Bill and I started". It was a wonderful, poignant moment and is a great source of encouragement and fortitude in many hours of, sometimes, sheer despair. Jon is a wonderfully entertaining fellow and a lifelong friend of Bill's and it was a privilege and joy to meet him.

I digress slightly; Bill wrote the words "Thanks, John, for having me over. Keep up your good work, and temper what you read with your own judgement. If what you see conflicts with what you read, believe what you see", in the front of a signed copy of his own superb book[1] he kindly presented to me as a gift. Bill chose these words aptly, on observing what stage I was at, on the introduction of the new concept of 'smoke burns' and I do not think it could have been put more clearly.

Bill's observation that the **thermal ignition temperature (T.I.T) of carbon monoxide (CO)** is approximately $660°C$[2] isn't just a little coincidental; it is,

---

[1] Clark, William E., "Fire-fighting Principles & Practices" 2nd edition (New York, 1990).

[2] Clark, William E., "Fire-fighting Principles & Practices" 2nd edition (New York, 1990).Page 16.

also, the recorded temperature of most 'lean flashovers' in the ceiling of a fire room compartment. I believe it is indeed the carbon monoxide igniting spontaneously at 660°C, which induces the flame front to run across the ceiling of a fire room compartment, as can be observed by fire-fighters at close quarters.

Some years ago, I had to give testimony to a coroner's court, following a fatal fire, at which, I was the Fire Investigation Officer. En route to the hearing with my senior officer at the time, I asked him what he thought of my fire investigation report, to which he replied, it was very good and did I have a copy of the report, I replied no, I gave it you, oh dear we concluded, neither of us had brought a copy and it was to late to about face and go and retrieve the report. Upon arrival at the courtroom, proceedings swiftly began, with several forensic scientists with scientific degrees testifying by reading out verbatim, of their reports.

Luckily for us the lunch recess arrived, before I was called to the stand and I took this opportunity to approach the clerk of the court and explain my predicament, to which she was very sympathetic and provided me with a Photostat copy of my report provided for the Coroner by the Fire Service. This particular copy had several denotations in pencil and upon closer examination these proved to be the questions the Coroner was going to ask me whilst on the stand. What a result, I approached the stand with renewed confidence and felt at ease throughout the process. Suitably pleased with my performance before the Coroner, I was about to sit down when the solicitor for the family of the deceased quite rightly chose to cross-examine my report and testimony and clarify the conflicting conclusions on the fire development between my report and that of the scientific experts. The lawyer challenged the validity of my testimony and expertise compared to the scientific witnesses who had previously been on the stand. My response was to ask him whether, apart from my Senior Officer observing at the back of the court, has anyone else in the courtroom ever been in a real fire? The Coroner accepted my version of events and the family of the deceased began the process of closure with a realistic understanding of the fire development in this particular fire in which their loved one had sadly died.

All I was taught in my own country from a scientific perspective, regarding fires, never seemed the same as when I was in a real fire "up close and personal".

It was not until I was fortunate enough to visit Sweden, on an educational visit with the Yorkshire and Humberside Branch of the Institution of Fire Engineers (IFE) in 1990, that I began to understand it was correct to –

BELIEVE WHAT YOU SEE

Swedish Educational Visit - 1990

Before our educational visit to Sweden in 1990, I'd believed the scientific explanations in our Manuals of Firemanship, United Kingdom (UK), that fire was basically a chemistry event. However, after three days of having my world turned upside down by Swedish fire-fighting theories and techniques, I now believe fire to be first and foremost a physics event. If you can take control of the 'air flows' of a fire you will be truly in charge of subsequent events for probably the first time in your career as a fire-fighter, rather than as previously, running into the building on fire and chasing the fire from A to Z...hoping to catch it before it reaches Z.

The name of the game is:

'AIR MANAGEMENT'

There now seemed to be a conflict between my academic understanding of fire and practical fire-fighting and to try and understand these contradictions and present a simple answer to this newfound dilemma, I began to study 'The Fundamentals of Fire'[3] an excellent book on fire development. The challenge to the status quo had begun.

How does bromochlorodifluoromethane (BCF) a vaporising halogenated hydrocarbon liquid, formerly used in fire extinguishers in the UK put out a fire? The scientific answer is "it has the property of interfering with the chemical reaction of flame propagation in the burning material"[4]. What on earth does that mean? It might sound good and get you through oral questions in the old fire service promotion exams, but what is it saying?

As a student in a fire officer chemistry class, on a course at The Fire Service College (FSC), Moreton-in-Marsh (UK), I asked our scientific lecturer taking the class to expand on the extinguishing capabilities of BCF.

Following the predictable textbook response, from the Manual of Firemanship, I posed another scenario. If indeed, BCF had these qualities, how, then, does steam extinguish a fire in a closed up fire room compartment, in exactly the same way as BCF does, when steam has already been through a chemical reaction of changing from a liquid to a vapour? I did not get a response and subsequently went on to fail my Chemistry paper at the FSC.

---

[3] Giselsson K., Rosander M, "The Fundamentals of Fire" GIRO-brand ab, (Sweden, 1978).

[4] Manual of Firemanship: Elements of combustion and extinction.
Book 1, Her Majesty's Stationary Office (London, 1974) Page 107

The Swedish Fire and Rescue Services theories and explanations made far more sense to me and related better to what I'd see in real fires. In my opinion, both BCF and steam simply extinguish the fire inside a closed up fire room compartment by the over carburetion of the combustible gas mixture with inert gases and the displacement of any remaining oxygen, resulting in the fire being extinguished, because it can no longer burn. In layman's terms, there is too much inert gas to support the decomposition and combustion process.

The birth of 'Over carburetion' was upon us and a new way of defining a 'rich' mixture was beckoning.

In unravelling these contradictions and developing a new theory, which supports the fact 'smoke burns', I feel a massive step forward in the fire-fighters understanding of fire development has been taken and we no longer have to restrict our knowledge of flashovers and backdrafts by referring to one single paragraph from the British Standard, "a sudden transition to a state of total surface involvement in a fire of combustible materials within a compartment",[5] describing the phenomenon of flashover.

On behalf of the fire-fighters of the world I'd like to take this opportunity to collectively thank the Swedish Fire and Rescue Services for their wonderful gift to us all, which has given us a better understanding of fire development.

---

[5] BS 4422, British Standard Glossary of Terms Associated with Fire. Part 1 General terms and phenomena of fire, British Standards Institution 1987

PREFACE

What was your first tangible recollection of FIRE? I remember mine. It was a candle on fire in the science class at school. When the teacher placed the glass over the candle the flame flickered and died.

Photograph No.1.a. – Free burning candle

Please note these and any other experiments depicted should not be replicated at home, but only performed by suitably qualified personnel in appropriate risk assessed training facilities.

Photograph No.1.b. – Pint pot glass placed over a burning candle

Photograph No. 1.c. – Pint pot glass placed over a burning candle

Photograph No.1.d. – Flame extinguished inside a pint pot glass

Why does the flame go out? Because of the lack of oxygen! But, is there another factor in play, contributing to the extinguishment of the flame?

"Over carburetion"

The flames use up the remaining oxygen inside the glass, yet they still burn for a short while. This creates downward radiation onto the wax of the candle, producing flammable vapours (combustible gases) which burn. So, before being extinguished, there are combustible gases being produced and just before the flame goes out it seems to rise up the wick and turn all blue in colour before disappearing. The over carburetion of the combustible gases has taken place because the fuel/air mixture inside the glass cannot escape or openly burn off. If you accept this reasoning, the flame is extinguished by a combination of 'Over carburetion/Oxygen Deficiency' of the fuel/air mixture and not just because of a lack of oxygen.

Another interesting visual effect of the burning candle is the various colours reflecting out of the flame.

Photograph No. 2 – Free burning flame over a candle

There seems to be a gap from the surface of the wax and the base of the flame.

The base of the flame seems to be - **BLUE**

The upper part - **YELLOW**

In my opinion, simple is best. I can relate to what I see as follows: The gap above the wax of the candle contains combustible gases too rich to burn (an oxygen deficient layer has formed above the wax). The flame at the base contains rich combustible gases at their upper explosive limit (UEL). The flame in the upper part contains combustible gases that are lean and at their lower explosive limit (LEL).

Basically, the flammable range of these combustible gases is there for all to see, right in front of your eyes in glorious Technicolor – a physical indication of the fire which you must understand, if you want to successfully extinguish fires as fire-fighters.

When the glass is placed over the flaming candle, why does the flame above the candle rise up away from the wax and turn blue before being extinguished inside the glass?

The fuel/air mixture has turned rich.

Scientific opinions explain that the blue flame denotes carbon monoxide (CO) is burning, which I am sure is factual. But if more of it is burning because it is enclosed in a compartment, with the oxygen restricted (deficient), then it would follow that more carbon monoxide (fuel) is burning and hence, my assumption that blue = rich has some simplistic credibility.

Is any carbon monoxide burning in the yellow flame? If not, is this because there is an invisible carbon monoxide filter above the candle. Surely not, there must be traces of carbon monoxide burning in other parts of the flame. Carbon monoxide has a flammable range of approximately 12.5 - 74.2%[6] and is present in nearly all fires.

Carbon monoxide is slightly lighter than air and an **invisible, odourless and explosive combustible gas.**

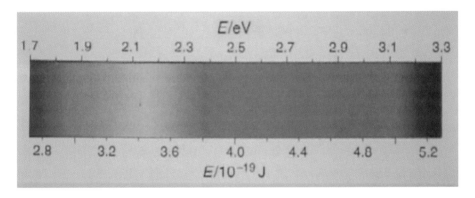

Photograph No. 3 – Spectrum Line

If we look at the Photograph No. 3 above and evaluate the spectrum line and relate what your eyes are seeing to the energy content of the visible colours, things become a little clearer. The colour of the flame directly reflects the energy content of the combustible gases burning, showing the energy of fuel rather than the type of fuel burning. This can be directly related to the flammable range:

Blue visible flame = 4.4 E/10 -19 J, yellow visible flame = 3.4 E/10 – 19 J.

---

[6] Cooke R. A., Ide R.H., "Principles of Fire Investigation" The Institution of Fire Engineers (1985), Page 297.

Basically, blue flames are reflecting more energy in light terms, which is equivalent to containing more fuel (combustible gases) – **rich** - and less air (oxygen). Yellow flames are reflecting less energy in light terms, which is equivalent to containing less fuel (combustible gases) – **lean** - and more air (oxygen).

This could lead us to apply the same premise to **black smoke**. The reflective energy of the colour black - 5.2 E/10-19 J - confirms the concept that black smoke inside a closed up fire room compartment is full of high-energy gases (rich) or at least elicits an acceptance that it has very little air in it and does not have sufficient oxygen to burn.

The train of thought expressed in the Preface is really to set the scene for a new approach and hopefully has got you thinking and challenging some long held concepts that might have outlived their usefulness. We shall see!

INTRODUCTION

Fire Development

Fire-fighters all over the world have three things in common;

1. We all advocate **FIRE IS UNPREDICTABLE.**
2. We all say we are the **BEST.**
3. We are all still losing fire-fighters to our common foe – **FIRE.**

When fire-fighters die in a fire, we turn to our comfort blanket - fire is unpredictable - and wrap it around us to protect us from our tragic loss. We march behind the Turntable Ladder (Aerial Appliance), to lay our colleague/friend/brother to rest and carry on:

> *"Half a league, half a league, half a league onward",*
> ....
> **"Their's not to reason why,**
> **Their's but do and die"** [7]

Senior Fire Officers are interviewed on television and comment on the unpredictability of fire. They state ours is a dangerous job and what brave fire-fighters the community are lucky to have.

I have never heard words like **"enough is enough".** If fire is unpredictable, we are admitting we do not know all there is to know about our enemy and, from now on, no more fire-fighters are going to die from a lack of knowledge, training or equipment.

One of my former Chief Fire Officers told me once, "fire-fighters will always die in fires, John, its part of their job", upon hearing this I politely excused myself and hurried to the personnel department and checked my contract carefully and thankfully, I could not find any such clause relating to this observation! My response to such comments is that it should be our collective professional goal to ensure fire-fighters do not die from the devastating effects of a backdraft or flashover in fires, with the only exception to this being because of human error.

---

[7] Extracts from Lord Alfred Tennyson's poem, 'The Charge of the Light Brigade' http://www.online-literature.com/tennyson/710/

The Fire Service/Department is a well disciplined service with highly skilled and dedicated staff and in my opinion the most life critical threat to this workforce is the loss of fire-fighters lives from the devastating effects of flashovers and backdrafts which sadly, is still occurring. Therefore, we have to work harder and smarter to find the solutions to bring to fruition this vision and a realistic study and research of the standard operating procedures (SOPs) am advocating in this book could be the catalyst to justify setting off on this journey, because fire is predictable and if we discover new knowledge and procedures, surely we are collectively duty bound to explore these new methods to evaluate if it can improve our current levels of fire-fighter in the line of duty deaths (LODD).

FIRE is PREDICTABLE

Upon arrival at an incident, fire-fighters with the correct knowledge, training and equipment should be able to read what stage the fire is at **(size-up)** and make a **diagonostic** decision on how to tackle the fire. You must get to "know your enemy".

On my research study travels. I met a fire officer in one particular UK Fire Brigade training department who had a picture of the Chief Fire Officer on his desk. I asked, "Why have you got such an item on your desk?" His reply was, that his Chief Fire Officer had visited last week and asked the very same question and he'd told his Chief Fire Officer that, Lieutenant-General (later Field Marshall) Bernard Law Montgomery (Monty) always kept a picture of Field Marshall Erwin Rommel (The Desert Fox) on his field desk, because he said you should always get to know your enemy!

To know your enemy, you must understand **FIRE** from A-Z and have a sound knowledge of the theory relating to **'smoke burns'.** Then you can apply your theories to integral standard operating procedures (SOPs), supported by realistic, responsible, practical training to maintain your competency.

New Theory – 'Smoke Burns'

If we identify the need to change by acceptance of this new theory, that 'smoke burns' and acknowledge that fire is the same globally, surely if we find a successful way to fight it, these techniques can be adopted worldwide.

New Standard Operational Procedures (SOPs) required

There will be a need to re-visit our existing standard operating procedures (SOPs) to enable us to deal with fires in an improved way in light of these new theories and to implement these new SOPs successfully and safely, there will have to be an identified 'Training Need' established for the transitional period.

"El futuro va a resultar mejor"

"The future will be better".

After the transitional period and when the required training has been completed and the standard operating procedures (SOPs) have been rolled out onto the streets. Fire-fighters' safety will be greatly improved, as will their knowledge and understanding.

"Taylor-Made" Solution

Once the training and operational systems of work are in place and National Occupational Standards (NOS) are created and competencies satisfactorily maintained, for both instructors and fire-fighters alike. We will have found the "Taylor-Made" Solution to this age old problem of the fire-fighters dying from the devastating effects of the various types of flashovers and be able to drastically reduce the current levels of in the line of duty deaths (LODD).

CHAPTER ONE

TERMINOLOGY

Part One – Pressure

"For every action – there is an equal and opposite reaction".

Sir Isaac Newton's third law of motion [8]

I remember a good example of Mr Newton's Principle, above, during a fire station Inspection by Her Majesty's Inspectorate of the Fire Service, who are usually former senior fire officers and can be quite pompous at times. Her Majesty's Inspector (HMI) came on parade and inspected the watch on duty. As he moved along the line of fire-fighters he halted at one particular fire-fighter, who at the time looked, like my good self now, a tad portly. The HMI quite abruptly said to the fire-fighter in question,

"Don't you think you are a little over-weight, young man?"

The fire-fighter replied, "Yes, sir, but I am doing something about it,"

HMI "Good, What is that then?"

Fire-fighter "I've joined a gym two weeks ago, sir and I have lost four pounds, already,"

HMI "Excellent, glad to hear it, so what was your original weight?"

Fire-fighter "Eight Pounds, Six Ounces, SIR"!!!!

I guess Isaac Newton had a point after all. The fire-fighter certainly did and answered admirably.

---

[8] http://www.grc.nasa.gov/WWW/K-12/airplane/newton3.html

Pressure plays a major part in every FIRE globally, with maybe the exception of a fire on Mount Everest and it is the same global atmospheric pressure, which keeps us all from floating off into space worldwide – 'gravity in effect'.

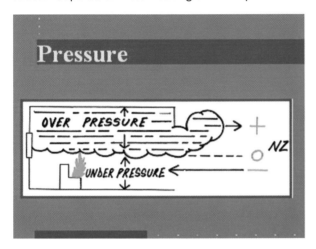

Figure No. 1 – Over Pressure, Under Pressure and Neutral Zone (NZ)

Figure No. 1 above depicts an armchair with flames emitting from it. What is on fire? Is it the chair? No it's the smoke/combustible gases.

Here lies the conundrum…either you do not call this substance smoke and call it combustible gases or continue to call it smoke and acknowledge that 'smoke burns'. These same combustible gases can be referred to as smoke.

A cigarette may have fallen down the side of the chair, causing the poly-urethane foam cushion to decompose producing smoke. Eventually the smoke mixes with the surrounding air and reaches the lower explosive limit and with the smouldering cigarette providing the ignition source the **smoke** ignites and begins to burn. The burning provides the sideways and downward radiation, which maintains the ongoing decomposition of the polyurethane foam chair. The smoke, being hot and buoyant and above atmospheric pressure, begins to rise towards the ceiling of the room.

This effect will be referred to as **'over pressure'**, because the smoke is above atmospheric pressure, 1 BAR (15 pounds per square inch) and is defined as POSITIVE (+) (over pressure).

Everything in physics tries to maintain a balance. When you place an item of food into the refrigerator, the cool air absorbs the heat given off from the item of food, until it equalises with the temperature of the fridge **(equinox).**

2

As the smoke on 'over pressure' vacates the open sided room, nature takes its course and tries to redress the balance. Air is sucked into the base of the flames, which will be referred to as **'under pressure'** because the air being drawn in at this low level is below atmospheric pressure (1 BAR) and defined as **NEGATIVE** (–) (under pressure). At the horizontal position where these two reactive zones meet at the bottom of the smoke layer and the top of the air layer, this will be referred to as the **'NEUTRAL ZONE' (0) (NZ).** The balance is equal at this point **NEUTRAL = 1 BAR. (0).**

If the 'over pressure' increases, because the flames begin to run along the ceiling, then the 'under pressure' will also increase to try and maintain a natural balance. The air flow will increase to the base of the flames and intensify burning at the seat of the fire, especially with an open sided room, which will result in an **'OVER-VENTILATED' FIRE**, as seen in the **'Stardust Disco Fire'**[9] re-construction video (Building Research Establishment, BRE). The direction of the air flow will be referred to as the **'air track'**. I had to think of a simplistic way of relating the movement of air and thought a reference to an 'air track', in a similar vein to a running track, would be appropriate.

The 'Stardust Disco Fire' re-construction at the BRE Cardington Laboratory Aircraft Hangar was not a true reflection of the real fire, because the external wall was missing to facilitate the filming of the re-construction, resulting in an inexhaustible supply of air.

A simple example of over/under pressure in action can be seen if you place a lit floating candle onto the surface of the water in a bowl, and then carefully place a glass over the top of it. You should then observe the flame rise up the wick, turn blue in colour and then go out. The other noticeable effect is that as the flame becomes extinguished, the floating candle on the water level inside the glass rises up above the water level outside the glass. What has happened after the flame has been extinguished?

The 'over pressure' above the free burning flame has converted to 'under pressure' as the enclosed compartment (glass over the candle) causes the flame to become extinguished, due to 'over carburetion/oxygen deficiency' because the combustible gases can no longer escape. As the flame goes out, the combustible gases cool and contract turning from positive to negative. The 'under pressure' created inside the glass, now allows atmospheric pressure outside the glass to force the water upwards, in exactly the same way a primer vacates the air in a fire pump casing, enabling water to be forced up into the casing from an open water supply.

─────────────────────

[9] http://www.bre.co.uk/fire/page.jsp?id=280.

This helps explain why, flames running the ceiling of a closed up fire room compartment are extinguished due to the 'over carburetion/oxygen deficiency' of the fuel/smoke. The pressure inside the room changes from 'over pressure' to 'under pressure' and begins to draw air into the room at a low level, via any gaps to the exterior, either under the door or around the window.

Part Two - Flammable Range (FR)

If you attended a house (structure) fire and the fire were still contained within the fire room compartment in which it started (e.g. the living room) and if as a fire-fighter you were asked to proceed down a corridor containing petrol vapours and open the door to the burning room, would you go ahead regardless of the petrol vapours? Or would you do something with the petrol vapours before effecting entry into the room? My guess is you would not open the door to the burning room before you immediately got rid of the petrol vapours because you can smell the fumes and acknowledge the danger there is in the flammability of these fumes.

However, if the same scenario above prevailed with light grey cold static smoke in the corridor, instead of petrol vapours, that you could stand up in, see clearly in and breathe mostly, odourless, colourless and explosive carbon monoxide, would you feel safe to open the door to the burning room in these circumstances?

The flammable range of petrol vapours is a well established concept, especially for us, would be do-it-yourself (DIY) motor mechanics, who, are forever searching for the optimum mixture by tweaking our car's carburettor to find yet more economy from our fuel consumption. It is also fair to say the concept of over carburetion (too rich) of the carburettor is not new and a fairly expensive folly.

I do not believe we truly understand 'smoke burns', because, if we did, the British Fire Service would not persist in using breathing apparatus guidelines (a piece of string with knots on it, denoting direction of travel) through grey smoke, a flammable atmosphere. Surely, standard operating procedures (SOPs) would state you must also take water with you for protection! What are we suppose to do, when this grey smoke ignites and burns, without any water?

If we understood that 'smoke burns' and are aware of the ignition sources and have the diagnostic ability to confirm that the ignition sources, are isolated from the fuel/smoke. Then, by applying **Tactical Ventilation with Positive Pressure Ventilation (PPV) Fans**, the smoke can be safely removed from the building. We can see what we are looking for and negate the need to use breathing apparatus guidelines forever.

The statement that, "We have always known 'smoke burns' for years. You are not telling us anything new, John", has been a constant companion on my travels at many presentations, made generally by Senior UK Fire Officers.

Their explanation of actions to be taken upon entry to the burning fire room compartment, containing invariably hot smoke would be to cool above them as the only effective method of making entry being to apply a water branch/ nozzle on a straight stream setting to hit the ceiling upon entry, which would effectively disturb any loose plaster hanging from the ceiling (lath & plaster) thereby preventing it from falling upon you as you proceed into the room. The straight stream jet directed at the ceiling of the fire room compartment turned into spray on hitting the ceiling and had a desired cooling effect, but was this done by design or good fortune, because, if it was deliberate, why not use spray in the first place? Regardless of the above, if it was known that 'smoke burns', then surely ventilating or cooling the grey cold static smoke in the corridor prior to entry would have been part of the standard operating procedures (SOPs) (even though they weren't called that in those days!).

If there was nothing new in the concept 'smoke burns', why are fire crews committed into burning buildings, ending up with only a piece of string with knots on it and no water for protection?

The tragic loss of three British fire-fighters, two fire-fighters at Gillander Street, London (1991) and one fire-fighter at Leo's Supermarket, Bristol (1996) whilst deployed laying breathing apparatus guidelines would suggest to me our concept that 'smoke burns' is a very narrow one at best.

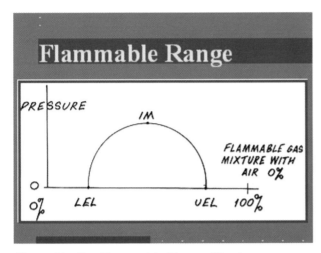

Figure No. 2 – Flammable Range Chart

Figure No. 2 above, shows Pressure on the vertical axis and Flammable Gas Mixture with Air 0 - 100 % on the horizontal axis.

LEL = Lower Explosive Limit (LEAN)
IM   = Ideal Mixture (Stoichiometric Mixture)[10]
UEL = Upper Explosive Limit (RICH)

The flammable range chart denotes the points at which the fuel/air mixture will ignite in the presence of an ignition source at the lower explosive limit (lean), which is a relatively low position on the pressure axis.

If the fuel/air mixture is allowed to go past the lower explosive limit and reach the vicinity of the Ideal Mixture (IM) before introducing an ignition source (delayed) then the position on the pressure axis is much higher and will ignite with the greatest force.

Once the fuel/air mixture has reached the upper explosive limit (rich) and if subsequently ignited it is once again relatively low on the pressure axis.

The interesting thing to note from this chart is that the fuel/air mixture cannot burn even in the presence of an open ignition source if it is either below the LEL or above the UEL, because the mixtures would be either too lean or too rich respectively.

---

[10] Cooke R. A., Ide R.H., "Principles of Fire Investigation" The Institution of Fire Engineers (1985), Page 296

Part Three – Combustible Gases

There are generally two classes of combustible gases to be aware of;

• **Normal Combustible Gases and**
• **High-Energy Combustible Gases**

NORMAL GASES

Their flammable range is approximately 50 - 95%. They are produced from fibrous materials such as paper and wood. These gases will ignite at relatively low temperatures and have a low thermal ignition temperature. The energy content of normal gases is 1000 Kj/Nm³ being a typical figure.

If these combustible gases ignite at their ideal mixture, the force of the blast will be in the region of 1 bar pressure, which could possibly blow out a window, or blow a door open.

HIGH-ENERGY GASES

Their flammable range is approximately 20 - 60%. These gases are produced from materials such as polyurethane foam, oil, plastics, bitumen, paints and rubbers. They require more oxygen to burn. Since they have large carbon rich molecules they are not easy to ignite. The energy content of high-energy gases can reach 15,000 Kj/Nm³. The energy content figures can be compared with methane gas, for example, which generates 35,000 Kj/Nm³. High-energy gases are flammable in a cold state and flashovers involving high-energy gases can be sudden and violent, if these gases ignite at their ideal mixture (25%), we are talking of pressures in the region of 8 Bars, which, in addition to causing possible fatal injuries to fire-fighters, could actually cause structural damage.

If combustible gases are heated up – what effect will this have on the flammability of the combustible gases?

Their flammable range will expand down towards 0% flammable gas mixture with air.

Why?

If you imagine, that the diagram on the left hand side of Figure No 3 below (See Page 9) to be a lit gas oven, that has not been preheated (cold) and as the combustible gases are injected into the oven, with an open ignition source present, these combustible gases do not ignite spontaneously, even with an ignition source present, because the cold air inside the gas oven absorbs the

7

energy of the combustible gases and they will not become flammable until the cooling effect of the cold air has been nullified and the flammable gas mixture with air reaches it's lower explosive limits and then they can ignite.

Conversely, if you actually pre-heated the air in the gas oven, prior to injection of the combustible gases, the cooling and energy absorption capability of the air would be negated, because it will no longer be cold and already warm and the combustible gases could this time ignite spontaneously, upon injection into the gas oven, because the lower explosive limit of the flammable gas mixture with air has gone down from it's original position (See Figure No 2) towards zero on the flammable gas mixture with air axis of the graph.

May be it is easier now to understand, that conversly, if we cool the combustible gases with water spray droplets of a small enough size that are projected through the combustible gas layer with force, the droplets will absorb the energy of warm combustible gases and similarly have a cooling effect and the energy conversion will transfer the heat from the flammable gases to the water mist, which will in turn expand and convert into water vapour or steam and will begin the 'over carburetion/oxygen deficiency' process by absorption of the energy and displacement of any oxygen present with steam (inertia) and with a lowered oxygen concentration the upper explosive limit drops towards the lower explosive limit and the fuel/air mixture becomes non-flammable when the two limits coincide (See Figure No 2).

Heat absorption inside a closed up fire room compartment reduces the decomposition and combustion process and heat can be absorbed by either air present at the early stages (maintaining the fuel/air mixture below its lower explosive limit), the introduction of an inert gas or water mist (shrinking the upper explosive limit of the fuel/air mixture down towards the lower explosive limit creating a non-flammable atmosphere) or indeed at a later stage of the fire by the fuel rich mixture itself (maintaining the fuel/air mixture above its upper explosive limit).

Part Four

Ignition Sources

As already pointed out, even if the fuel/air mixture is within its flammable range it cannot burn until it has been ignited.

There are three basic types of ignition sources:

1   Open
2   Closed/Concealed or
3   Intermittent

Open Ignition Source

Figure No 3 – Open Ignition Source

1. Open Ignition Source

This is basically a naked flame that is already present, such as, lit matches, burning gas ring, burning candle etc. Figure No. 3 above shows ignition will occur at the lower explosive limit. If you have an **open ignition source** a flaming candle or open flame, the combustible gas/air mixture will not ignite as soon as the combustible gas e.g. Liquid Petroleum Gas (LPG) is introduced from an opening on the left hand side of the room. It has to mix with air, in enough volume to reach the lower explosive limit, before ignition, which in these circumstances, is at a relatively low pressure.

The same is true for smoke collecting in the ceiling of a closed up fire room compartment. The armchair/bed has been giving off smoke from a heat source, a smouldering cigarette. The smoke reaches its flashpoint[11], ignites and produces flames, which give off sideways radiation, decomposing the furniture further. The smoke then rises on 'over pressure' into the ceiling and even though there is already an open ignition source present, the smoke in the ceiling does not ignite immediately. It has to collect in enough volume to reach its lower explosive limit, after which the flames can now ascend up through the smoke (flammable gas mixture) into the ceiling and spread towards all four corners of the fire room compartment.

The increase in flame-up produces downward radiation on a massive scale, which causes everything combustible below the flame front to decompose and produce more smoke (combustible gases). If the room is closed and windows remain intact, the subsequent **'LEAN FLASHOVER'** will only last 5-15 seconds in a normal size room, before the flames in the ceiling are extinguished by the culmination of over carburetion (too rich) and oxygen deficiency.

Closed/Concealed Ignition Source

Figure No. 4 – Closed/Concealed Ignition Source

2. Closed/Concealed Ignition Source

This type of ignition source is called closed or concealed because a flame (ignition source) is introduced after the flammable gas/air mixture has gone

---

[11] Cooke R. A., Ide R.H., "Principles of Fire Investigation" The Institution of Fire Engineers (1985), Page 297.

past the lower explosive limit or come down from the upper explosive limit and is progressing towards the ideal mixture when this type of previously closed/concealed ignition source is released.

E.g. the immersion heater in an airing cupboard has a short circuit which creates a spark, which falls onto some towels stored in the airing cupboard and they begin to decompose and produce smoke (combustible gases), that subsequently ignites and starts to go through the **'mechanism of fire'** and creates an airing cupboard full of black smoke and smouldering towels. The bedroom/adjacent room has light grey smoke in the room that is relatively cold and in which you can still see and breathe.

The Fire Service/Department arrives and fire-fighters are deployed with breathing apparatus and a hose reel branch/nozzle to extinguish the fire. They enter the room and locate the fire in airing cupboard by feeling the heat transmitting through the door with the back of their hand. They open the door to the airing cupboard whereupon the black smoke, formerly rich, vacates the airing cupboard into the upper part of the room on 'over pressure' and in so doing increases the flammability of the combustible gases in the room, which are now progressing rapidly towards the ideal mixture. The smouldering fire in the towels also becomes visible as the smoke vacates the airing cupboard.

Now the fire-fighters, do as they have been taught and hit the base of the fire disturbing a brand (a previously closed or concealed ignition source) which is picked up by the 'air track' and taken straight into the smoke/air mixture in the upper half of the room. This creates a subsequent **'Delayed Flashover'**. The fire-fighters get their ears singed and have a bit of a laugh back at the Fire Station/House on this seemingly harmless little deflagration.

The reason they have survived is, that, you do not find many people with a polyurethane foam armchair in their airing cupboard. The towels inside the airing cupboards emit low-energy normal gases and, as such, do not have as much energy or explosive force as high-energy gases. If a fire involving a decomposing polyurethane foam chair/bed were similarly treated, these standard operational procedures (SOPs) used above could, and have, resulted in fire-fighters being seriously injured or even killed.

A closed/concealed ignition source can ignite a gas/air mixture anywhere on the flammable range!

Intermittent Ignition Source

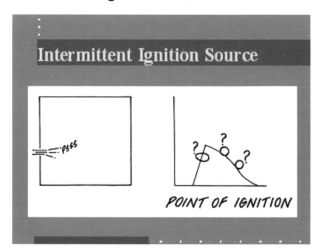

Figure No. 5 – Intermittent Ignition Source

3. Intermittent Ignition Source

This type of ignition could be a spark from a short circuit on an electrical appliance. It can occur at any time and anywhere on the flammable range. However, it is unlikely to cause ignition inside a closed up fire room compartment after it has gone past the lean flashover stage and has become too rich.

DESKTOP BACKDRAFT & FLAMMABLE RANGE SIMULATOR

The desktop backdraft and flammable range simulator below (See Photograph No. 4), designed by Fire Instructors Training Products Ltd[12] is capable of demonstrating all three types of ignition sources and lean flashovers, backdrafts, 'delayed flashovers' and 'fire gas explosions', superbly and is an excellent visual tool to demonstrate these theories and assists in developing the required the knowledge and understanding.

Photograph No. 4 – A 'fire gas explosion'

Photograph No. 4 depicts the visual effect of a 'fire gas explosion', which has ignited the combustible gases inside the box at their ideal mixture and exploded, subsequently the combustible gases have expanded three to four times their volume and forced the side door and 'fail safe' ceiling to blow open.

If you look at Photograph No. 4 above again and in your minds eye imagine the ceiling was not 'fail safe' to open and all the energy from this 'fire gas explosion' was concentrated on the only remaining exit port (door). Then you can imagine how much more devastating the effects of this type of explosion would be if this scenario occurred inside a fire room compartment in a house/structure?

---

[12] www.fitp-ltd.com

Goran Cederholm☺ (Swedish Fire Engineer)[13] demonstrated to me whilst visiting Uppsala Brandforsvar on a research trip the benefits of the Aquarium Box – The Swedish equivalent of the Desktop Backdraft and Flammable Range Simulator and it is a great visual way of consolidating your knowledge and understanding of these theories.

---

[13] In my opinion, my good friend Goran is one of the best and most knowledgeable Swedish 'Flashover Instructors'. I had the privilege of first meeting Goran and another good friend Mats Granat (Swedish Fire Engineer) in 1993 and we have shared many interesting discussions on the designs of Fire Development Simulators (FDS) and the marvellous diesel flashover simulator in use by Uppsala Brandforsvar is Goran's brain child and well worth a visit.

CHAPTER TWO

The 'MECHANISM OF FIRE'

We have now dealt with the terminology used, relating to 'smoke burns' and move on to the theory of fire development. The previously used, singular description of a flashover (See Page xiv) was no longer applicable by 1995, because of the realisation that there were six different types of flashovers, which can occur in nearly 95% of fires. A thorough understanding of the 'mechanism of fire' from A to Z is the desired prerequisite for all fire-fighters and they must obtain an in-depth knowledge and understanding of fire development.

Part One

Fire Development

Fire has been with mankind an awfully long time and can be a good servant, but a terrible master. Both mankind and fire are living, breathing forces of nature. However, we have one thing the fire does not have, a brain, and we should beat it every time and NEVER again allow it to seriously injure or kill one of our own kind in the performance of their noble task. We must learn to beat the fire with our brain and not just our heart, by beginning to understand fire from A to Z, get to know our enemy and outwit it, and study its every move until we are able to predict it's next move on every occasion after our arrival.

"FIRE IS PREDICTABLE"

In my opinion, once the Fire Service/Department arrives on the fire-ground, the fire, should not get any worse and we need to develop our 'size-up' skills, to be able to 'read the fire gases', diagnose which stage it is at and predict where it could go. Then we should head it off by getting in front of it, instead of running into the building/structure and chasing it from A towards Z.

In Figure No. 6, below, we can see a fire room compartment with a double glazed external window intact and closed. The door of the room is also intact and closed. There is a corridor outside the room with a double glazed external window, intact and closed. Adjacent to the corridor is an inverted flammable range chart to evaluate the various horizontal positions of the smoke layers, to enable us to begin to appreciate how you can read the flammability of this smoke layer, by interpreting its horizontal position in the fire room compartment.

A cigarette is dropped down the side of the polyurethane foam armchair. The heat from the burning cigarette decomposes the polyurethane foam

15

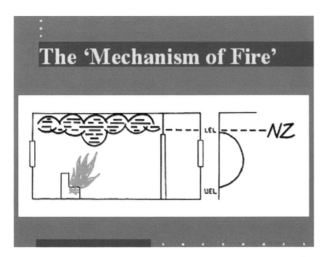

Figure No. 6 – The 'Mechanism of Fire' (A to Z)

and combustible gases (smoke) are given off and they soon reach their low explosive limit near the closed/concealed ignition source, the smouldering cigarette, and a flame is produced, which now creates decomposition on a greater scale because of the sideward radiation from the flames.

These decomposed high-energy combustible gases (smoke) rise upwards on the 'over pressure' and begin to collect in the ceiling of the fire room compartment and gradually increase in volume, because the fire room compartment is closed and therefore, the combustible gases (smoke), cannot escape out of the room. The combustible gases (smoke) begin to back up and gain more and more volume and are progressively becoming more flammable, because they are rapidly approaching their lower explosive limit.

This is why the flame begins to get higher, because the heat from the original flames is also heating up the combustible gases adjacent to the flames, which are rising up the 'air track' into the ceiling. As already pointed out, if we heat up the combustible gases, this will make them more flammable by widening the flammable range and lowering the flammable gas/air percentage it's original lower explosive limit (LEL) down towards 0% flammable fuel/air mixture and eventually they expand to reach their thermal ignition temperature.

Therefore, these combustible gases (smoke) ignite from the open ignition source already present (flames) and the flames begin to rise and expand through the combustible gases (smoke) via the 'air track'.

Simultaneously, the combustible gases (smoke) in the ceiling are reaching their lower explosive limit (LEL) and once, they connect and flame runs over the ceiling. We have reached the **'lean flashover'** stage. So called because the flammable gas/air mixture is lean, and the fire flashes over the ceiling. The stage at which these combustible gases/smoke become flammable is when the smoke layer banks down from the ceiling and reaches the point on the inverted flammable range chart at their LEL, approximately at the level adjacent to the top of the door. However, just prior to reaching the LEL, the gases were not flammable and the fire was still at floor level.

During the filming of the 'Under Fire' television programme[14] in which I was fortunate enough to be a participant, I placed a chair away from the wall and set it alight. This was in order to dispel some existing perceptions in the British Fire Service, that it was the flammability of the chipboard (fibreboard) wall linings used in Swedish houses that was creating more combustible gases (smoke) and faster flashovers. It was previously thought that there is not the same probability of such flashovers in the UK because of our non-combustible plasterboard (gypsum) wall linings.

The time taken from ignition to the 'lean flashover' stage, was three minutes and fifty five seconds, without any flame impingement onto the chipboard (fibreboard) wall linings, proving that these flammable linings did **not** contribute significantly to the speed and subsequent power of this particular 'lean flashover'.

Even with non-combustible UK wall linings, a polyurethane foam chair positioned in the corner of the room against these non-combustible wall linings, would go through exactly the same burning process with air only available on two sides, instead of four, in fact the process would go even faster, because of what is known as the 'elongated flame' effect. The flames being produced cannot escape or dissipate heat as easily and the heat being created is localised and intensifies the sideways and downward radiation, which in turn increases the de-composition of the polyurethane foam chair producing more combustible gases (smoke) burning upwards on the 'over pressure' which nature tries to balance by increasing the 'under pressure' and sucks more air into the base of the flames on the 'air track' and a way we go. The energy content (calorific value) of the decomposing material is a major contributing factor to the speed and force of the fire development (flashover).

This also brings into question the validity of the 'rate of surface spread'[15]

---

[14] The Equinox TV programme, produced for Channel 4 (UK) (1995) by Kilroy Television, (programme number 21491), also shown on the Discovery and National Geographic TV Channels in over 24 countries worldwide.

[15] British Standards BS 476: Part 7:1997. 'Method of test to determine the classification of the surface spread of flame of products'.

testing procedures, which establish how far an 'elongated flame' will travel along the surface of a product. Because, if it is the combustible gases (smoke) on fire and they travel upwards into the ceiling, uniformly and downward and sideways radiation is one of the major contributing factors to fire development, by decomposing everything combustible in the fire room compartment and the combustible gases (smoke) being produced float away from the surfaces and up toward the ceiling with buoyancy. What relevance has the observation of how far 'elongated flames' travel across the surface of a product, in a laboratory setting?

The energy content of the de-composing product, producing combustible gases (smoke), is far more relevant, because it is not the product on fire, but rather the combustible gases (smoke) and because the dynamics of the combustible gases (smoke) produced will be similar, but their energy content will be different. The length of time a flame takes to travel across a surface maybe irrelevant, when in a real fire inside a closed up fire room compartment. The flames travel uniformly across the upper parts of the room having usually left the floor level from the original seat of the fire.

In fact, if you accept that it is the smoke burning (combustible gases) and they are hot and buoyant and float away from the surfaces of combustible materials and linings on the 'over pressure' being lighter than air. Then, why do we in the UK need five different classifications of fire?[16]

How do free burning combustible gases (smoke) produced from the decomposition of fibrous materials (wood, paper etc) that burns differ from the smoke burning from decomposed flammable liquids?

Surely it is the smoke (combustible gases) on fire and the only discernable difference is the calorific value of the flammable material decomposing and there are only two real classes of fire, these being free burning smoke (combustible gases) on fire or non-flaming smouldering fires e.g. metal fires. Electrical fires are dangerous, whilst the power supply is still flowing, but once isolated and the residual current is earthed, it becomes either a free burning fire or a smouldering fire.

---

[16] http://www.communities.gov.uk/pub/417/SleepingAccommodationfullguide_id1500417.pdf
Page 58 Fire Safety Risk Assessment - Sleeping Accommodation Department for Communities and Local Government (2006) .

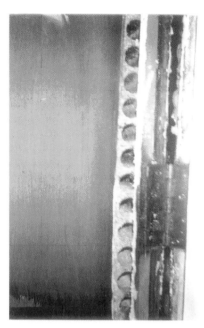

Photograph No. 5 - A 'tube board' fire-resisting door with hollow tubes in the chipboard (fibreboard) inners

Additionally, the credibility of fire testing of fire doors must also be brought into question, because in my role as a Fire Investigation Officer for another fatal fire I examined the fire scene to discover that the fire-resisting doors on the internal fire protected staircase had chipboard (fibreboard) inners with hollow tubes. This type of door construction, using what is known in the industry as a 'tube board' core, is a common method of manufacturing fire doors. The core is formed from chipboard (fibreboard) which, is extruded to give hollow tubes of various diameters running across the width of the leaf (See Photograph No.5).

The fire occurred in a House of Multiple Occupation (HMO), residential bed sits with common facilities e.g. kitchen, laundry etc, shared by various occupants on three levels. The original seat of fire was in the front ground floor (UK) bed sit and broke into the internal fire protected staircase because the fire room compartment door remained open. The investigation established that from the time flames entered the internal fire protected staircase, activating the ground floor hallway smoke detector, until flames were issuing from the second floor (UK) (front) bed sit window (were a resident was rescued by the fire crews using ladders), having burnt through two sets of fire doors and non-combustible partitions at second floor level, was twelve minutes.

The fire resistance rating for the two sets of second floor fire doors and fire resisting partitions (plasterboard/gypsum) was 30 minutes (60 minutes in total). Yet, fire crews rescued a gentleman hanging out of the second floor window with flames licking around his ears. The flames had only taken twelve minutes to reach the second floor window once inside the internal fire protected staircase.

How can this be?

The sight of chipboard (fibreboard) inners on fire doors admittedly shocked me, especially as I had also been the Specialist Fire Safety Inspecting Officer for this particular building and completed a Fire Prevention Report in our agency status for the local council and I was concerned that I might have missed the inserting of non fire-resisting doors into the premises. I double checked the original Fire Prevention Report and with the assistance of the Environmental Health Department of the Local Authority (enforcing authority) established through the Warrington Fire Research Station that the fire doors installed into this HMO met the British Standards (BS)[17] for fire-resistance, successfully tested to give 30 minutes integrity performance and had done so with chipboard (fibreboard) inners.

The use of the phrase 30 minute fire-resisting doors is rather misleading and I believe the testing criteria for fire resistance is in urgent need of reviewing or the terminology currently used should be redefined to truly reflect the performance of these type of products, achieve during fire conditions in a real fire scenario.

Now, I was horrified, having spent the previous eight years facilitating realistic fire training in Fire Development Simulators (FDS) using 2.44 metres (m) x 1.22 m x 12.5 millimetres (mm) chipboard (fibreboard) sheets to create the required fire development training and simulated flashovers, because of the effectiveness of chipboard (fibreboard) decomposing and providing ample high-energy combustible gases (smoke) for the training scenarios. I was dumb founded to discover, that the very same chipboard (fibreboard) was being used as infill for supposedly fire resisting doors, which had passed the British Standard (BS) for fire-resistance.

---

[17] British Standard BS 476:Part 22:1987 'Methods for determination of the Fire-resistance of non-load bearing elements of construction.

Photograph No 6 – Fire Development Simulator (FDS) pre-loaded with 2.44m x 1.22m x 12.5mm soft board sheets used as wall and ceiling linings

The loading scenario above (See Photograph No. 6) is exactly the same format for use with chipboard (fibreboard) and medium density fibreboard (MDF) sheets. We, sometimes use MDF sheets during cold weather, because it burns faster than chipboard (fibreboard) sheets and reaches the 'lean flashover' stage quicker. MDF sheets have a British Standard BS 'rate of surface spread'[18] Class 1 rating, which means it can be used as wall lining in open plan shop floor areas (UK).

I began to look deeper into these anomalies. I rang the Department of Environment (D of E), who were responsible for fire resistance testing at the time, to discuss my concerns. The fire-resistance test for fire doors, which entails the door on test being placed in a furnace and the outer side of the door observed to see how long it is before flame penetrates through the door. If this does not occur for a minimum of 30 minutes, then the door is deemed to satisfy and passes the BS fire-resisting test and gets a 30-minute integrity rating. I asked the gentleman that I'd rang at the 'D of E' if anyone had ever placed a match to the combustible gases (smoke) being produced on the non-furnace side of the door to see if these combustible gases (smoke) ignited and hence spread the fire. There was a long pause then the gentleman put the

---

[18] British Standards BS 476: Part 7:1997. 'Method of test to determine the classification of the surface spread of flame of products'.

phone down on me.

The problem at this particular fire in a House in Multiple Occupation was that the flames had entered a fire protected internal staircase and these flames rapidly decomposed the glue (formaldehyde) in the chipboard (fibreboard) used as infill for the fire resisting doors at first and second floor level (UK). This produced massive amounts of high-energy combustible gases (smoke) sustaining the fire spiralling up the staircase. An external window on the fire-protected internal staircase in between first and second floor level also failed and provided additional air to these massive amounts of high-energy combustible gases (smoke), leading to an effect similar to a flame-thrower onto the fire resisting doors and partitions at the head of the staircase on the second floor. This brings into question the assumption that a "30 minute fire-resisting door" will resist and prevent fire passing through it in realistic conditions for 30 minutes.

How can it be said to resist fire if the smoke being produced on the other side can be ignited and spread the fire beyond the fire-resisting door and partition?

I raised my concerns at a Fire Investigation Seminar with some eminent UK fire experts present and they seemed reluctant to 'grasp the nettle' and resolve this ludicrous situation. Fire resisting doors should not have chipboard (fibreboard) (held together by glue) as an integral part. These doors should be completely fire resisting and, more importantly, smoke production free.

For this to be achieved in a practical scenario of a real fire they should not produce combustible gases (smoke) on the risk-free side of the door. Any doors or partitions wanting to be deemed fire resisting, in my view should not only prevent flame penetration, but also, should not produce smoke (combustible gases) on the risk free side, because this smoke could easily be ignited by an ignition source and contribute to further fire spread on the other side of the fire resisting wall/partition. The solution, may be to develop a realistic fire resistance test for these building materials, incorporating a test criteria for smoke production on the risk free side and thereby, being able to use proven products to create a realistic and completely integral fire-resting compartment and prevent fire and combustible gases (smoke) from spreading to adjacent risk free escape compartments.

Part Two

LEAN FLASHOVER

Whilst, visiting my good friend Jim Mastin ☺ [19], Chief Fire Officer of Livingston Fire and Rescue Department. Montana. United States of America (USA) I gave a presentation to a group of fire officers and Gary Clutter (my friend and ski partner at Bridger), Training Officer for Bozeman Fire and Rescue Department asked me, "How does the 'lean flashover' work?" When it looks the wrong way around and upside down using the flammable range chart inverted on its side, the smoke (combustible gases) seems to be filling up the fire room compartment from the top down. It was a great question.

Well, if you compare fire to be the opposite of water, you might be able to take the 'leap of faith' needed. Water takes the least line of resistance and falls downwards when released, because it is heavier than air so gravity will take it to find its natural level. If water were poured into a glass, it would fill up from the bottom to the top.

FIRE is "t'other ways about"…as we say here in Yorkshire. Smoke (combustible gases) is lighter than air and moves upwards when released into the atmosphere. The smoke (combustible gases) rises up into the ceiling and fills the room up, uniformly with smoke (combustible gases) from the top down. This is why I inverted the flammable range chart, to enable fire-fighters to understand the links between the position of the smoke layer to the flammable range chart and therefore, its relevance to its flammability and explosive potential. As the smoke (combustible gases) fills up the room from the top down, it is exactly the same as water filling up in the glass from the bottom, but vice versa.

This is the beginning of a better understanding of why the horizontal position of the smoke layer (neutral zone - NZ) in the compartment/building can give you a clear visible physical indication of the flammability of the smoke layer and what stage of development the fire is at between A – Z.

Before we move on, I'd like you to consider the following: at the early stages

---

[19] I met Jim and my other old mucker from Virginia – Warren Whitley (Fire Marshal) at a training event at Prince William County Fire and Rescue Service, Virginia, USA in 1994 and we have been good friends ever since and their wonderful families have always shown me the rest of the Taylor clan wonderful hospitality and kindness, during my annual pilgrimage to the USA. We have also shared lots of interesting discussions on 'smoke burns' and both Jim and Warren have assisted me tremendously with the production of this book, for which am eternally grateful. I try to visit Jim in Montana every winter to chat to the troops and get my annual skiing fix at Bridger Mountain and Big Sky ski resort, catching Warren on the way back via Washington DC.

of the fire described thus far, consider the next stage of the fire if the windows and doors of the fire room compartment stay intact and remain closed. The fire room compartment ends up full of black smoke and there are no yellow/blue flames showing. Was there fire in the ceiling before the fire suffocated, or not?

The British Home Office responsible for the Fire Service in the United Kingdom at the time carried out tests by using the Fire Experimental Unit Still-Air laboratory at Little Rissington to evaluate fire development in a closed up fire room compartment, but the photographs from the tests and the accompanying text state these are from an enclosed room fire. I looked long and hard at these photographs because the images did not seem consistent with my understanding of the 'smoke burns' theories.

But, remember things are not always as they seem, which was demonstrated vividly to a fire-fighter from Manchester, UK, who was also as a part-time taxi driver (cabbie) and had the privilege one evening of picking up Tommy Cooper (a very funny British Comedian) from Piccadilly train station and taking Tommy to the Midland Hotel as it was known at the time. They arrived at the Midland Hotel and exchanged pleasantries and the fare for the ride, Tommy, just before getting out of the taxi, leant through to the front of the cab and placed something into the top pocket of the cabbies shirt and tapped the pocket saying, "Have a drink on me. It's been a pleasure meeting you". The cabbie could not wait to see if Tommy had given him a fiver (£5 note) or a tenner (£10 note) as his tip, but he remained polite and did not look in Tommy's presence and waited until he brought his taxi to an abrupt halt around the corner from the hotel and promptly delved into his shirt pocket to find a tea bag!

The images of the fire development unfolding, on Page 16 of the Fire Service Manual:[20] Compartment Fires and Tactical Ventilation, Volume 2, were consistent with a constant air supply and certainly not those of a limited air supply in a closed up fire room compartment. It made me look twice, only to discover the door to the side of the fire room compartment, appeared to be open as clear as the daylight coming through it. If you look carefully at the first picture of the tests (top of page 16) it seems that the door to the room is in the open position.

If the door to this room had been closed, instead of open, then there would not have been the same amount of fire development depicted in the pictures taken during the tests.

---

[20] Fire Service Manual: Compartment Fires and Tactical Ventilation.
Volume 2, Fire Service Operations, HM Fire Service Inspectorate Publications Section, London: The Stationary Office (1997) Page 16.

I believe another experiment should be carried out by the Fire Experimental Unit, but with the door closed this time. You would then be able to conclusively evaluate, whether there are flames running along the ceiling, prior to the fire being suffocated and entering into the 'quiet phase', providing that the experiment was carried out in a single fire room compartment with a double-glazed front fire-resisting glass partition to accommodate the observation and the door closed.

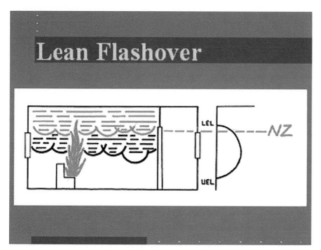

Figure No. 7 – 'Lean Flashover'

The first of six different types of flashover is the **'lean flashover'.**

In approximately 95 % of fires inside a closed up fire room compartment that remains in tact, flames will flashover the ceiling before the fire suffocates and dies down, leaving the fire room compartment full of black smoke. In the other 5% of fires, where this does not occur, it is because the original heat source decomposing combustibles has not produced enough smoke (combustible gases) in the ceiling to facilitate the 'lean flashover'. For example, a rubbish bin on fire in the middle of the room with the flames not impinging on other combustible materials in the room will, thereby not be producing enough smoke (combustible gases) (volume) in the ceiling to reach its lower explosive limit, before the fire in the rubbish bin runs out of fuel and burns out.

Once the fire flashes over the ceiling, massive amounts of downward and sideways radiation occur, decomposing everything combustible adjacent too and below the flame-front. This produces large amounts of smoke (combustible gases) and with the fire room compartment closed up. The 'lean flashover', now running the ceiling only lasts 5 -15 seconds in a normal size room, before the flames in the ceiling are extinguished by the combination of 'over carburetion/oxygen deficiency', created by the black smoke (combustible gas) layer. With the flames in the ceiling now extinguished the subsequent combustible gases (black smoke) cool and begin to contract back into the walls/ceilings linings and create an 'under pressure' which, then sucks air into the fire room compartment through any gaps under the door or around the windows. The air travels towards the lowest level via the 'air track' to the seat of the fire (chair/bed). If this item of furniture or combustible material does not have the ability to smoulder, then the whole process is finished, because without the ability to smoulder there is no longer an ignition source present within the fire room compartment and the original seat of fire is extinguished. All you are left with is a room full of black smoke, but without an ignition source inside the fire room compartment.

However, if it does have the ability to smoulder we move into the next phase of fire development, in which the fire begins to 'breathe into life'.

Before we move on to that stage it may be beneficial to ponder on how a sprinkler works.

The fire starts at low level. We eventually have the 'lean flashover' and it is at this stage that the sprinkler bulb bursts because of direct flame impingement approximately above 68°C. Once the water leaves the sprinkler head and hits the deflector, turning it into water spray droplets, which immediately begin to absorb energy and cool the combustible gases/smoke shrinking the upper explosive limit down towards the lower explosive limit (See Page 8). In effect, it prevents the fire from running across the ceiling, which in turn prevents the most influential factor to rapid fire spread downward and sideways radiation from the fire running across the ceiling.

To emphasise the point, if the sprinklers were turned off, then the fire would be allowed to run across the ceiling, unchecked. Sprinklers reduce the temperature of the combustible gases/smoke and create the desired inertia, which prevents the 'lean flashover'. The water spray droplets contain the fire; they do not put out the fire at floor level. This, once again, is conclusive evidence that the 'smoke burns' theories are the truth. If you cool the combustible gases/smoke, it will shrink and reduce their flammable range.

'LEAN FLASHOVER' IN A FIRE DEVELOPMENT SIMULATOR (FDS)

Photograph No. 7 – 'Lean Flashover' in a Fire Development Simulator (FDS)

If you examine Photograph No 7 above you will observe, that the kindling fire in the right hand corner of the Fire Development Simulator (FDS) has de-composed the chipboard (fibreboards) being used as wall and ceiling linings and the 'lean flashover' is beginning to flashover the ceiling towards all four corners of the fire room compartment. There seems to be 'white smoke' around the edges of the flame front, which is actually steam being produced from the moisture in the fibreboards and after all the moisture has evaporated into steam, it no longer inhibits the glue (formaldehyde) and more high-energy combustible gases (smoke) are released increasing the speed of the 'lean flashover' running the ceiling.

In my opinion, if an onboard sprinkler system had been fitted as standard on all aircraft, the devastating effects of the Manchester Airport aircraft fire disaster in 1984[21] might have been drastically reduced by the sprinklers cooling the smoke (combustible gases) inside the fuselage. This may have inhibited the combustible gases/smoke being produced inside the fuselage, as a result of the radiated heat from the fuel fire outside the fuselage, from reaching their

---

[21] http://www.aaib.gov.uk/sites/aaib/cms_resources/dft_avsafety_pdf_502609.pdf

lower explosive limit and may have delayed the subsequent 'lean flashover' in the ceiling of the fuselage long enough to have possibly allowed all the passengers and aircrew to have evacuated safely.

If the 'lean flashover' had been delayed by the activation of an integral on-board sprinkler system and a facility fitted to enable the Fire Service upon their arrival, to augment the supply via designated external inlets to boost the onboard water supply. Then the biggest contributing factor to the rapid-fire development, the downward and sideways radiation onto rows and rows of high-energy polyurethane foam chairs and plastic racking, could have been slowed down. Once this downward and sideways radiation took hold, the amount of high-energy gases being produced led to a rapid-fire development across the ceiling of the fuselage. With the doors of the fuselage open for evacuation purposes, there was a constant air supply travelling along the air track contributing to these disastrous consequences.

You can liken the 'lean flashover' downward and sideways radiation scenario, to that of a chip pan fire, but upside down. In a chip pan fire, we have a pan with flammable oil in it. The heat from the flames (gas ring cooker) below and around the sides of the pan causes the oil to heat up and cook the food placed into it. Once the oil is heated too much and the smoke (combustible gases) being produced above the surface of the oil reach their thermal ignition temperature they will ignite on contact with air. The flammable vapours given off now feed the flames continually; the oil is being heated from below and above, but mainly from below.

What is the first thing you are taught to do in a chip pan fire?

Turn the heat supply off.

Why?

By turning the flaming gas ring off (heat source) and reducing the heat supply to the oil, it limits the decomposition of the oil considerably and then, when you place a rung out damp towel or fire blanket with great care over the pan and isolate the air supply, it should be extinguished and not re-ignite on the removal of the cover at a much later stage. Members of the public should never attempt to remove a chip pan that has been involved in a fire that they have been successful in extinguishing by smothering it with a rung out towel or fire blanket, because of the tendency for it to re-ignite, if the towel or blanket becomes dislodged during removal of the pan to outside of the premises, which may cause the person carrying the pan to drop the pan and the boiling oil onto their lower body causing extensive burn injuries.

Please always leave it in situ on the cooking appliance to cool and await the arrival of the Fire Service/Department.

The 'lean flashover' is similar to the chip pan fire, although in this case it is like the chip pan fire turned upside down. The heat source the fire-fighter has to prevent is running across the ceiling of the room, creating massive amounts of downward and sideways radiation which is producing the fuel, which is feeding the fire. So before we go for the fire at low level, we must first prevent the production of more fuel by cooling the flames running across the ceiling, which you cannot always see due to the thick black smoke layer running just below the flame front in the ceiling.

Part Three

OVER CARBURETION/OXYGEN DEFICIENCY

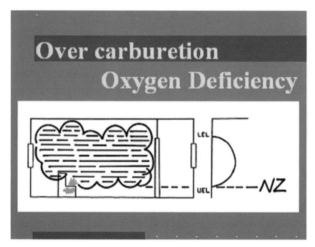

Figure No. 8 - Over carburetion/Oxygen Deficiency

The window will fail in a closed up fire room compartment during the 'mechanism of fire' either during the 'lean flashover' because of direct flame impingement (single pane window) or at a later stage of the fire because the negative pressure inside the room drops below atmospheric pressure outside and the window is forced inwards (double glazed window).

However, Figure No.8 above shows that it is possible for the flames to be extinguished due to 'over carburetion/oxygen deficiency' after they have directly impinged on the glass, because in this instance we are demonstrating a double glazed window. The inner pane could well crack from direct flame impingement, but before the outer pane can fail, the flames in the ceiling of the fire room compartment have been extinguished by 'over carburetion/oxygen deficiency'.

29

For further confirmation of the concept of 'over carburetion/oxygen deficiency' study Photograph Nos. 8a, 8b, 8c, & 8d, below:

Photograph No.8.a. – Glass placed half over a burning candle

Place a glass over the lit candle on a holder, but this time keep the glass from touching the base plate.

Photograph No. 8.b. - Glass placed half over a burning candle

Air can get in at the base of the glass, free to travel towards the flame. The flame has all the air it needs to burn. So does the flame continue to burn or does it go out?

Photograph No. 8.c. - Glass placed half over a burning candle

The flame rises up the wick, turns blue in colour and then goes out. The combustible gases (carbon monoxide) are collecting in the top of the glass and slowly filling the glass full of combustible gases exactly the same as if we were to turn glass right way up and fill it from the top with water, only the other way about. You can't see this easily, because carbon monoxide is an odourless, colourless and explosive combustible gas.

Photograph No.8.d. - Flame extinguished inside glass placed half over a candle

The combustible gases on 'over pressure' have collected at the top of the glass and slowly filled up the glass compartment. They sink down onto the flame above the candle. These are at a higher pressure ('over pressure') than the air trying to enter the glass on 'under pressure' and even with air seemingly freely available the flame is extinguished, because the flammable mixture inside the glass is now too rich to burn. This proves the major effect in play here is over carburetion of the fuel and not seemingly a lack of oxygen. The fuel rich mixture has displaced the oxygen on 'over pressure'.

What effect would a closed up fire room compartment full of black smoke (combustible gases) seemingly to rich to burn and oxygen deficient, have on the decomposition and combustion process inside the room? The fuel rich mixture can displace the oxygen and absorb energy required for the decomposition process, effectively extinguishing the fire by a combination of 'over carburetion/oxygen deficiency'. If you accept this as a plausible explanation and that the concept that the absorption of heat (energy) reduces the decomposition and combustion process because all the heat (energy) is being absorbed by the fuel rich mixture.

Would it be practical for fire-fighters upon arrival at a house/structure fire with a closed up fire room compartment full of black smoke, to use these circumstances to their advantage and maintain the fuel rich mixture by not letting air into the fire room compartment?

In my opinion it is a viable option and worth exploring the practical implications of incorporating this tactic into the standard operating procedures (SOPs), which I shall return to discuss later, giving you time to consider its feasibility.

Hence, we can now, move on to the fire 'breathing into life' stage before the free flaming, full room fire stage.

Part Four

FIRE BREATHES INTO LIFE

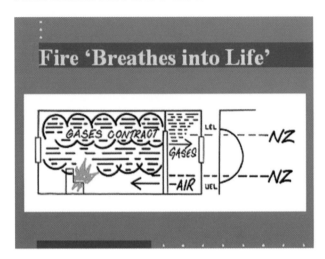

Figure No. 9   The fire 'breathes into life' stage

After the flames in the ceiling have been extinguished because of 'over carburetion/oxygen deficiency', the heat in the ceiling decreases and the smoke (combustible gases) contract back into the walls and ceiling linings. They begin to contract and create a vacuum, which sucks air into the closed up fire room compartment via any gaps around the doors and windows.

Previously, the flames directly above the combustible materials (original seat of fire), which were contributing to the decomposition and combustion process are now, also extinguished due to the 'over carburetion/oxygen deficiency' of the fuel/air mixture and an oxygen deficient layer (atmosphere) is maintained directly above the combustible materials during this now, smouldering process, which is still decomposing the combustible materials and producing some combustible gases (similar to the oxygen deficient layer created above the wax of a burning candle – See Photograph No. 2), maintaining an oxygen deficient layer above the smouldering material. The air now enters on the 'air track' and travels towards the oxygen deficient layer formed above the surface of the smouldering material during the quite suffocated phase and dilutes the adjacent flammable gas/air mixture just below the upper explosive limit (See Figure No.9 for the horizontal position of the lower NZ) making it momentarily flammable. This enables the smouldering fire to flame-up in the flammable gas/air mixture directly above and around it.

33

Following flame-up, this downwards and sideways radiation produces more combustible gases/smoke, some of which are forced out of the fire room compartment on 'over pressure' around the gaps at the top of the door into the corridor. The majority of the smoke (combustible gases) cannot escape and remains inside the closed up fire room compartment. They accumulate and bank down, forcing the flammable gas/air mixture above the upper explosive limit and become too rich to burn. This sequence is now repeated and the fire seems to **'breath into life'** with smoke pulsating into the corridor around the gaps between the door and frame, providing a visible sign, clearly indicating which stage this particular fire is at.

Part Five

PULSATION CYCLE

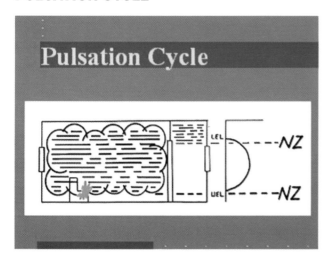

Figure No.10 - Pulsation Cycle

The pulsation cycle, which has now begun is a positive and negative cycle and eventually, if on the negative cycle it goes below 1 bar atmospheric pressure (15 pounds per square inch), the window can be pushed inwards by atmospheric pressure and not because of heat.

Part Six

NEGATIVE MODE

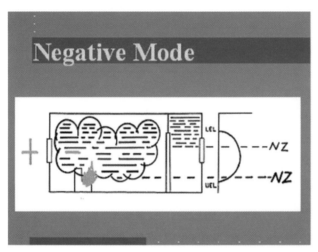

Figure No.11 – Negative Mode of the Pulsation Cycle

Why is the smoke accumulating in the corridor **GREY** and the smoke inside the closed up fire room compartment **BLACK?**

The smoke is black inside the fire room compartment because this denotes that the flammable gas/air mixture is rich with fuel and oxygen deficient. As it is forced out into the corridor it has changed from black to grey, because it has mixed with air in the corridor and becomes diluted, which also cools the previously hot black smoke. Similar to mixing black and white paint, you end up with a grey colour.

As can be seen in Figure No.11 above, we now have two separate horizontal positions of the neutral zones (NZ) on the inverted flammable range chart and as the grey smoke (combustible gases) accumulates in the corridor it is getting closer to the ideal mixture. The cold, grey, static, breathable smoke could be high-energy combustible gases from the decomposition of polyurethane foam furniture mixing with air in the corridor and the longer the call to the Fire Service/Department is delayed the hotter the black smoke (combustible gases) inside the possibly double glazed windowed fire room compartment becomes and simultaneously are getting closer to their thermal ignition temperature, whilst the grey smoke (combustible gases) is accumulating in more and more volume in the corridor and is becoming more and more flammable.

If fire-fighters arrive and open the door to the closed up fire room compartment and the black smoke (combustible gases) inside is at its thermal ignition temperature the black smoke (combustible gases) vacates the fire room compartment on 'over pressure' and produces a flame on contact with air (open ignition source) in the top half of the corridor where the grey smoke (combustible gases) in the corridor is in close proximity to their ideal mixture. It is like striking a match and igniting a 'delayed flashover' which could expand 3 - 4 times its volume and hit the floor and ceiling simultaneously before taking the least line of resistance (like water) and vacating the premises via the corridor to fresh air.

To assist with 'size up', we must begin to 'read the fire gases': if you open up the front door to a house/structure and observe there is a cold grey smoke layer approximately in a half way horizontal neutral zone position in the corridor and has no movement (static), what does this tell you about the flammability of the smoke layer?

Cold grey static smoke[22] indicates a flammable (lean) and/or possibly an explosive environment (ideal mixture).

What does the lack of movement of the grey smoke layer tell you about the door to fire room compartment?

No movement indicates that the door is closed. Because, if after opening up the external door to the house/structure and allowing the introduction of air from outside on the 'air track' has not resulted in any change in the movement (buoyancy) of the grey smoke layer, because the air is not able to reach the seat of the fire and force the black smoke inside the fire room compartment outwards to the front door. This gives you visible confirmation that air is not getting to the seat of this fire, because the door to the fire room compartment is **closed.**

Additionally, these circumstances confirm that there is no ignition source in the grey smoke layer. Therefore, with the ignition source (seat of the fire)

---

[22] Conversely, warm grey smoke moving with force and exiting a building/structure on 'over pressure' indicates that the 'lean flashover' has not yet occurred in the fire room compartment because there is already an exit port (window/door opening) available for the grey smoke to vacate the building/structure, thereby preventing the accumulation of fire gases in the ceiling of the fire room comapartment, because all the various inter connected compartments inside the building/structure and the internal doors leading to the seat of the fire are open. These circumstances usually appertain to fire room compartments at the lowest point of the building/structure e.g. basement, which also prevents the rising smoke from accumulating and reaching its lower explosive limit (LEL) . A good visual analogy of this scenario is the warm grey fast moving smoke emitting from a smoke chimney stack from the smoke box of a steam train, it has power and movement but there are no flames present, because there has not been a 'lean flashover' in the smoke box.

separated from the fuel (grey smoke), it is now safe to secure around the fire room compartment by ventilating the fuel (smoke) in the corridor or creating inertia by applying water spray droplets into grey smoke layer.

Control of the 'air flow' is the way to go.

Part Seven

BACKDRAFT

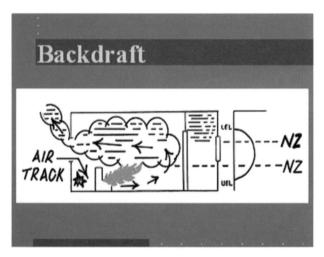

Figure No.12 – Backdraft (Ventilation Induced Flashover)

The second type of flashover is called a **'backdraft'**.

The window fails on the negative mode of the pulsation cycle, because the negative pressure inside the fire room compartment is below atmospheric pressure and atmospheric pressure forces the window inwards. Air can enter the previously closed up fire room compartment on the 'air track'. The smoke (combustible gases) begins to evacuate the room via the window (exit port) on 'over pressure'. As the air comes in down and around, it disturbs the oxygen deficient layer formed above the surface of the smouldering material (ignition source), producing flame-up and simultaneously diluting the previously rich flammable gas/air mixture adjacent to the smouldering material down below its upper explosive limit, making them flammable. As the ignition source flames up, the flames can begin to travel through the smoke (combustible gas) layer towards the exit port along the 'air track' on 'over pressure'.

37

There are several descriptions for this type of flashover –

VENTILATION INDUCED Flashover etc. I have chosen **BACKDRAFT** as used in North America, because I feel it depicts it best, especially when air is sucked in and blows smoke and fire out (backdraft), plus, it is inclusive and an acknowledgement for our former and current commonwealth cousins, colleagues and friends over the other side of the pond (The Atlantic).

Part Eight

MOBILE PULSATION CYCLE

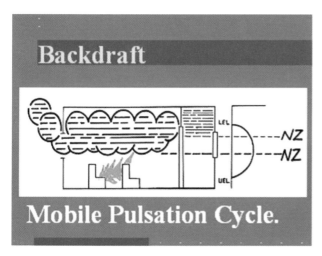

Figure No.13 – Backdraft – Mobile Pulsation Cycle (Positive Mode)

A clear visible sign of an impending 'backdraft' is pulsating black smoke at a window or door (exit port).

An opening in the fire room compartment is created either by failure or opening of the window or door (See Figure No. 13). Air enters on the 'air track' following the path of the 'under pressure'. This disturbs the oxygen deficient layer formed above the surface of the smouldering material (ignition source), producing flame-up and simultaneously diluting the previously rich flammable gas/air mixture to below its upper explosive limit, making the smoke (combustible gases) adjacent to the flames just flammable. These now begin to burn and force flames towards the exit port on 'over pressure'.

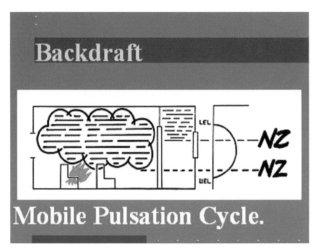

Figure No.14 - Backdraft – Mobile Pulsation Cycle (Negative Mode)

However, if this flame-up causes the flames to impinge on another combustible item, e.g. an adjacent polyurethane chair (See Figure No. 14) this sideward radiation will create large amounts of smoke (combustible gases), which will be greater in volume than the volume of air entering on the 'air track'. This creates a 'back pressure' and momentarily makes the combustible gas/air mixture too rich to burn, it effectively dies down and it loses its momentum. This is evident at the exit port by the black smoke, previously exiting, visually seeming to be sucked back inside the opening and creating the illusion of pulsating. In reality the black smoke has just lost its momentum and momentarily stopped forcing black smoke out on 'over pressure'.

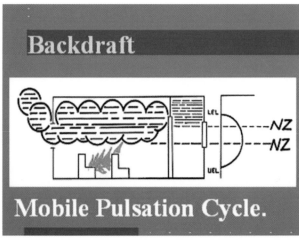

Figure No.15 – 'Backdraft' – Mobile Pulsation Cycle (Positive Mode)

As the air continues to flow into the fire room compartment it dilutes the flammable gas/air mixture some more and it burns up again similar to inside a closed up fire room compartment described earlier, only on a larger scale (See Figure No.15).

Now we have what I describe as a mobile pulsation cycle travelling through the flammable gas/air mixture on the 'air track' towards the exit port and looking as if it's pulsating. As these pulsations get less and less frequent, this is a clear indication the air is overcoming the fuel production and the flame front is getting increasingly closer to the exit port.

When I presented a 'Flashover Training' paper at the FIRE '93 International Fire Conference in Glasgow, Scotland. A Fire Engineer delegate asked me, "What was the frequency of these pulsations?" my response was, "I do not know, but all I need to know as a fire-fighter on the fire-ground is, that as those pulsations get less and less the flame front is getting nearer and nearer the exit port". The significance of my response was to recognise the meaning of the visual signal of the pulsations, if I have opened up the front door to a house/ structure involved in fire. The indication of an impending backdraft - black smoke pulsating at the front door tells me I need to buy myself some thinking time and by simply closing the front door I can put the fire back into **neutral** and go back to square one. If the external door has not been demolished and unhinged in the breaking in sequence!

Control of the **'air-flows'** is the name of the game.

Part Nine

BACKDRAFT – CLEAN BURN

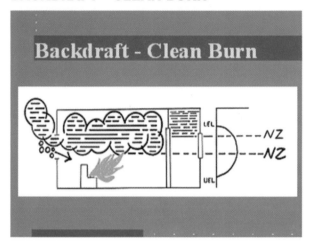

Figure No.16 – Backdraft – Clean Burn

A clean burn 'backdraft' is when an opening is created by the failure or opening of a door or window of a previously closed up fire room compartment in the over carburetion/oxygen deficient stage and this time there is no back pressure it is a clean burn with rapid burn up and dilution of the flammable gas/air mixture. Hence as it burns up, it increases the speed of the 'over pressure', vacating the fire room compartment via the exit port. Nature tries to be balance this by increasing the 'under pressure' to compensate. This can be visibly identified by the bottom layer of the black smoke exiting on the 'over pressure' being dragged back into the opening by the vacuum created by the 'under pressure' entering into the fire room compartment via the lower part of the opening.

A clean burn 'backdraft' will be extremely fast and a lot quicker than a pulsating 'backdraft'. In fact the pressures created by such backdrafts can suck fire-fighters down staircases if the door leads to a basement closed up fire room compartment at the over carburetion/oxygen deficient stage. It is also important not to open fire room compartment doors too far or wide, during application of door entry techniques because, depending on which way it opens, it will either be too hard to physically close the door against the strength of the 'over pressure' or the speed of the 'backdraft' can lead to loss of control of the door and inability to close again to restore stability. This will allow the fire to run amok throughout the building.

'Air Management' is the key to unlock this particular door.

CHAPTER THREE

THE FREE FLAMING STAGE

Part One - FULL ROOM FIRE

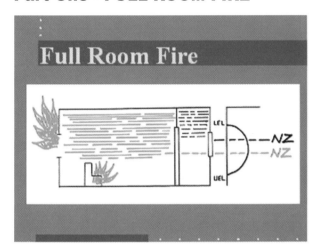

Figure No.17 – Full Room Fire

A pulsating or clean burn 'backdraft', eventually will both lead to a free flaming full room fire if left to progress unchecked, now, with an unlimited oxygen supply and the rich mixture diluting progressively towards the ideal mixture and sufficient fuel inside the normal size fire room compartment depicted in Figure No. 17 above and full downward and sideways radiation, we have arrived at the scientific definition of the flashover stage (See Page xiv). The position of the flame front is extremely informative to fire-fighters if they understand the effect of pressure on the smoke/combustible gases and flames.

If fire-fighters arrived at a house/structure on fire with the flames issuing from the ground floor (UK) window (lounge) burning freely approximately half way up the window, is the door to the fire room compartment open or closed?

Ask yourself where the air supply for this fire is coming from?

Consider the horizontal positions of the 'over pressure', 'under pressure' and the 'neutral zone'. If the flames on 'over pressure' are in the top half of the window, then the 'under pressure' must be in the bottom half with the 'neutral zone' being where the two meet. Hence, air is going into the fire room compartment via the 'air track' in the lower part of the window, so the internal door to the fire room compartment could be either closed or partially closed. Alternatively, the door to fire room compartment may be **open** but all the connecting compartments and corridors external doors to fresh air will be **closed.**

Part Two

Use of the 'UNDER PRESSURE' Extinguishing Technique

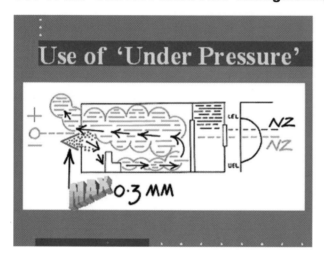

Figure No.18 - Use of the 'under pressure' extinguishing technique

If upon arrival fire-fighters have flames from the ground floor (UK) lounge exiting on 'over pressure' in the upper half of the window and the air flow going into the lower half on 'under pressure' down towards the ignition source, up into the flame front and back out to the exit port on 'over pressure', this constitutes an 'air track'.

How could you extinguish these flames in this full room fire externally from directly outside this window?

Use the 'appliance of science'. If you put small enough water spray droplets into the 'under pressure' region of the lower half of the window, surely these droplets would be picked up and travel along the 'air track' right into the flame front without any effort? Let physics do the work. Once these water spray droplets reach the flame front, they take away one side of the triangle of combustion, heat, and extinguish the flames by cooling. The efficiency of this operation depends on the size of the water droplet and the ability to travel through the flames at the correct pressure is critical to the extinguishing capability of the fire-fighting branch/nozzle in use. The introduction of small size water droplets via high-pressure branch/nozzles can support the provision of effective and safer fire-fighting techniques.

The maximum efficient water spray droplet size is approximately 0.3 millimetres (mm) delivered at a pressure of 6 Bars (90 pounds per square inch) as used by the 'Fogfighter' low pressure branch/nozzle, made by Tour Anderson (TA) of Sweden.[23] However, some Swedish scientists have advocated the ideal (optimum) water droplet size is 0.03mm delivered at a higher pressure of 133 Bars (2000 pounds per square inch) and the nearest I've come to using such a small droplet size was during trials and I had the privilege of using a high pressure branch/nozzle called the 'Blaster' designed by Gerry Harris, which produced a droplet size of approximately 0.03 mm[24] and has proved to be both the most efficient and effective water spray droplet size I've ever used so far.

I am currently an adviser to the Chief Fire Officer's Association CFOA (UK) Compartment Fire Behaviour Training (CFBT) National Practitioners' Group and at a recent meeting I was asked for my opinion on which type of branch/nozzle (weapon) was the most effective. My response was that the best type of weapon is one that creates the optimum size of water spray droplet (0.03mm) at high pressure to complement the application of these fire-fighting techniques. The water spray droplet size is critical, because the smaller the size then the number of water spray droplets will increase e.g. approximate number of water spray droplets for the various sizes:

Fogfighter	**Blaster**
0.3mm	0.03mm
(100 droplets)	(1000 droplets)

For the same amount of water the smaller size water spray droplets of the 'Blaster' can produce 900 more water spray droplets than the 'Fogfighter'. Hence when absorbing the temperature of the flames the larger water spray droplets will absorb more energy and heat than the smaller ones which will create subsequently more steam. The smaller droplets may dissipate the heat over the same surface area so much more efficiently, that they may not even rise above 100°C and turn into steam - they may in fact only heat up to about 80°C, and only reach a water vapour state, which would create a

[23] Giselsson.K. & Rosander,M, "Extinguishing with FOGFIGHTER".
(Tour & Andersson AB, Valve Division, Box 300, S-520 30 LJUNG.(Sweden.1994). Page.10

[24] Letter dated 30 March 1998, from Gerry Harris, Director, Blaster Technologies Ltd, Troon, Scotland.

more comfortable working environment for fire-fighters, with the additional advantage of being able to operate with a lot less water. These smaller water spray droplets also have the ability of shrinking smoke layers up away from the floor and improving visibility for the fire-fighters operating at floor level.

The effect of inserting water spray droplets into the 'under pressure' region is to instantly stabilise the fire and prevent it from running away from you (See Figure No 18). The fire will re-ignite but you have taken away its power without the production of massive amounts of steam elsewhere in the building. You have also prevented flames impinging upon the glass of upper floor windows above the fire room compartment, which could cause them to fail and allow a flame (open ignition source) into the upper floor where smoke/combustible gases could have collected some distance away from the fire room compartment. If this smoke (combustible gases) has gone past its lower explosive limit and become flammable it will ignite on the introduction of a flame exiting from the ground floor living room (fire room compartment) and the fire begins to spread and 'leap frog' the building.

The 'Under Pressure' extinguishing technique is just as effective on exterior fires adjacent to houses/structures, as it is on interior house/structure fires, indeed the faster the air intake on the 'under pressure' the quicker the water spray droplets will be taken to the seat of the fire and beyond into the flames via the 'air track'. The only discernable variable is the exterior fire will normally be larger and then you must apply the Peter Norell – rule of fire fighting[25] **'More Fire, More Water'.**

The maximum size water spray droplet size of 0.3mm would be suitable in these circumstances to provide the additional flow required achievable with a low pressure pump delivering 6 Bars. The 'Fogfighter' is capable of delivering 450 litres per minute and would be ideal for this task. This exterior fire, which, if the flames are impinging onto a structure and are left unchecked, could soon spread to involve the structure and result in also having to simultaneously deal with an interior fire, 'Size-up' of this fire should identify the air intake

---

[25] Peter was nominated as my translator on the 'Flashover Instructor' Course I attended at the Swedish Fire and Rescue College (Raddingsverket) at Sando, Sweden in 1991. We have been friends ever since and Peter and his lovely family have always made me and the Taylor clan welcome at their abode in beautiful Harnosand and I still treasure our friendship some 16 years later. Plus, Peter is the best branch/nozzle operator I have met in Sweden and when I set fire to that settee/sofa in the 'Under Fire' programme and sat there watching it reach the 'lean flashover' stage, it was not because I was brave or stupid, but secure in the knowledge that Peter would be on the branch/nozzle backed up by another good friend Tore Eriksson at the doorway with a 'Fogfighter' and I could trust them with my life. Indeed if you watch the part where Peter and Tore re-enter the closed up fire room compartment you will see the perfect application of the 'under pressure/over pressure' extinguishing techniques described on Page 48.

for the exterior fire and then the first strike crew should be deployed to put water spray droplets into the 'under pressure' region to stabilise or better still extinguish the exterior fire and limit the spread whilst other crews 'size-up' and 'read the fire gases' in the house/structure, to evaluate whether the fire has already spread into the house/structure and also become an interior fire.

'Size-up' the fire conditions in Photograph No.9 below:

Photograph No. 9 – Central Open Air Access Staircase to a residential apartment block fully involved in fire

Where is the air intake?

Can you clearly see the 'over pressure' and 'under pressure areas and where the two meet at the 'neutral zone'?

How could you stabilise this fire in seconds and stop it running away from you?

If you put the right size droplets with enough flow into the entire 'under pressure' region (approximately from the base of the staircase enclosure up to the first floor UK balcony level), ensuring that the water spray pattern (cone) covers this 'under pressure' region, then the water spray droplets would travel through to the seat of the fire and beyond into the flame front and knock down the large flames within seconds. Let physics do the work and 'read the fire gases' and diagnosis what they are telling you and then base your tactics on informed decisions.

There are various North American Fire Departments who have protocols that instruct fire-fighters that fires should not be fought from the fire side. In light of the application of the 'under pressure' extinguishing techniques may be it is time to revisit these particular procedures and research and evaluate the benefits under certain fire conditions of using this technique, especially if limited resources are available on the first attendance.

I intend to explore the application of the 'under pressure' extinguishing technique from the exterior of buildings/structures by examining some case histories, evaluating whether its application could have resulted in a better outcome, in my forthcoming book –

'Size-up'- Fire-fighting Tactics.

And on our website:

www.smokeburns.com

Another good friend of mine from the USA, Joe Starnes[26] has filmed hours of house/structure burns during training evolutions in an attempt to understand these theories and am sure subconsciously to try and disprove them and cling onto old long established traditional concepts, which is the right thing to do, because any fire-fighter worth their salt would not just take my word

---

[26] Joe Starnes is a former Volunteer Fire Chief of Sandy Ridge Fire Department, Charlotte, North Carolina, USA. I met Joe at a New Jersey hotel in 1994 with Jim Mastin and I proceeded to show Joe my power point presentation on "Flashover Training", shortly afterwards Joe turned around and jokingly, called me the 'anti-Christ' stating that I had just turned upside down all he previously had been taught about fire development. Joe then went back to Sandy Ridge and began to film training exercises in real house burns to evaluate the theories and SOPs and some 20 hours of filming later, he called me to confirm his worst fears and reiterated his first impressions. I am hopeful that Joe will let us post some of this footage on our website for educational purposes and provide an article outlining his experiences. Our families have become good friends over the years and in 2005 I had the privilege of presenting "Smoke Burns" to the crews at the Sandy Ridge Fire Department and Joe kindly took me and my youngest son Tom, to see the Bobcats play the New York Knicks. One distinct observation he expressed to me was that during the filming of the flame front from the window of a kitchen on the ground floor (UK) at the rear of the house/structure, with the front door to the house/ structure and the kitchen door both open, the flame front was from the bottom of the kitchen window sill upwards, identifying the air intake was coming from below the window sill, hence air must be entering on the 'air track' via the open front door on the 'under pressure'. Joe states, that as soon as the fire-fighting crews were committed through the open front door he noticed the flame front at the rear kitchen window psychically moved upwards away from the window sill towards halfway and was getting its air now from the bottom half of the window, because the fire-fighters entering through the doorway at the front door had effectively blocked the 'air track' and the flames had to find another air supply. Therefore, if you actually closed the front door presumably that would have the same effect and then you could feasibly apply the 'under pressure' extinguishing technique from the exterior of the house/structure through the kitchen window into the 'under pressure' region from the fire side and extinguish the fire.

for it, regarding these theories and they should want to see these standard operating procedures (SOPs) in action with their own eyes, just like I did, because you are not going to change the way you work, when your life depends upon it, until you have had the chance to test them out and know for sure that they work, which is where the training in the Fire Development Simulators (FDS) comes into play, but trust me it is a one way ticket once you've been inside a Fire Development Simulator (FDS) and seen it for real.

We have had experienced fire-fighters and officers enter the Fire Development Simulators (FDS) and come out and said "I've learnt more in fifteen minutes, than I have in my last fifteen years service".

Part Three

The 'OVER PRESSURE/ UNDER PRESSURE'
Extinguishing technique

How would you, as a fire-fighter tackle a free running fire in the ceiling of fire room compartment in which control of the 'air flows' has been lost and with door open and the flames with a massive black smoke layer below it rolling towards you at a fair rate of knots?

Extinguishing this flame front running at you, as a fire-fighter inside a fire room compartment, could be easily achieved by using the **'Over Pressure/Under Pressure' extinguishing techniques.**

Why is it we are advocating using 'under pressure' as an extinguishing technique externally from directly outside a window of the fire room compartment, yet, when we are inside the same fire room compartment dealing with the same type of flame front, we recommend using 'Over Pressure/Under Pressure' extinguishing techniques?

During a recent Chief Fire Officer's Association CFOA (UK) Compartment Fire Behaviour Training (CFBT) National Practitioners' Group meeting I elaborated upon another myth brought home from Sweden by British CFBT Instructors, this being that small squirts of water spray droplets introduced in pulses into the flame front in the 'over pressure' region, known as spotting or pulsing, in the Fire Development Simulators (FDS) (containers) is enough to control the flame fronts in real fires. In my view this is a misconception, that may originate from the early days of compartment fire behaviour training (CFBT) in the converted steel freight containers in the UK, when this technique was used to demonstrate control and shrinking back of the flame front with only a minimal amount of water spray droplets and it was an extension of the theories taught in the laboratory to prove the validity of these new techniques.

The technique of spotting/pulsing is effective in the controlled environment of the UK Fire Development Simulators (FDS) the vast majority of which have a relatively small vent at the top of the simulator. A contributory factor to the spotting/pulsing technique being effective in these scenarios is the rich flammable gas/air mixture environments created by the use of a small top vent.

However, in a real house/structure fire inside a fire room compartment with high-energy combustible gases (smoke) burning from the decomposition of polyurethane foam furniture and a flame front running across the ceiling at you and the door is open to this fire room compartment, spotting/pulsing has the potential to get you and your fire-fighting partner into serious difficulties. In my opinion it can be an inherently dangerous practice in adverse conditions and has never formed part of the fire-fighting techniques used by Swedish Fire and Rescue Services (Brandforsvar) on their fire grounds.

In fact, my Swedish fire-fighting colleagues advocated the use of 'over pressure/under pressure' extinguishing techniques the very first time we met in 1990. There are various reasons for this, which will become apparent as I describe the actual technique to which am referring.

As we have seen, the use of the 'under pressure' extinguishing technique externally is tremendously effective by following the 'air track' all the way round and cooling the flames from the seat of fire to the exit port on the 'over pressure'. Therefore, why will this not be as effective at close quarters inside the fire room compartment?

The water spray droplets introduced into the 'under pressure' region, just above the fire room compartment floor, will also force the flame front away from the seat of the fire on the 'air track' before it catches the flames up, cools and extinguishes them. Inside a fire room compartment this can be disastrous and force the flame front into the facemasks of the fire-fighting crews and if the face visors of the fire-fighting crews breathing apparatus sets are not **glass** and just the normal polycarbonate visors, they could melt and fail, resulting in fatal circumstances for the fire-fighters.

When this technique is used from the exterior, the flame front is pushed away from the building/structure upward into fresh air and above the heads of the fire-fighters at the windows.

The Swedish fire-fighters advocate the use of 'over pressure/under pressure' extinguishing techniques whilst fire-fighting inside a fire room compartment, when fire-fighters are faced with a free running flame front of high-energy burning combustible gases across the ceiling of the fire room compartment and the door open.

The first term used in the title of this technique is 'over pressure'. A curtain of water spray droplets of the correct size (0.03 - 0.3mm) is first introduced into the 'over pressure' region, ensuring the angle of the spray hits both sides of the fire room compartment walls, to prevent the flame front in the ceiling going past the water spray curtain introduced as an extinguishing technique. This is crucial, because it prevents the flame front going past the fire-fighters and hitting the wall behind them, coming downwards and effectively cutting off their exit route.

The technique should be applied by opening up the 'Fogfighter' style branch/ nozzle fast and counting up to three or four seconds and then slowly closing the branch/nozzle back down and, in so doing, applying the correct amount of water spray droplets, preventing an effect known as 'water hammer' on the hose lines carrying the water from the fire-fighting pump to the branch/nozzle. This smooth action technique reduces to a minimum any sudden increases in pressure, which could inadvertently cause the water hose lines to burst and leave the fire-fighting crews without any water to extinguish the fire and facing a hasty and perilous retreat.

Fire-fighters should first apply 'over pressure' extinguishing technique as outlined above, followed seconds later by the use of the 'under pressure' extinguishing technique. Water spray droplets of the correct size (0.03 - 0.3mm) are then introduced into the 'under pressure' region, with the same smooth action technique, just above the floor of the fire room compartment, travelling along the 'air track' to meet the already introduced water spray droplets in the 'over pressure' region in front of the advancing fire-fighters.

The water spray droplets in the 'under pressure' region push the flame front towards the water spray droplets previously introduced into the 'over pressure' region and the two meet creating cooling on a massive scale and instantaneously shrinking back the flame front, creating a lull. This "window in time" allows the fire-fighters to advance slightly forward and prepare, as the flame front comes again, to repeat the process until they have shrunk the flame front in the ceiling back to the seat of the fire on the floor. Then, they apply water spray droplets in a straight stream format to paint the wall linings with water, preventing any further production of combustible gases from these linings which could re-ignite and finally use water spray droplets to extinguish the original seat of the fire (open ignition source).

Photograph No 10 – CFBT Instructors demonstrating the 'Over Pressure/ Under Pressure' extinguishing techniques in the Fire Development Simulator (FDS) at Manchester Airport Fire Service Training Ground

Whilst performing these techniques the fire-fighting crew should be in pairs inside the fire room compartment, with the lead fire-fighter holding and applying the water spray droplets and the other fire-fighter supporting by taking the weight and feeding the water hose line to the branch/nozzle as the lead fire-fighter advances. They should face the flame front (always face the enemy) on one bended knee and the other leg arched with the sole of their fire boot firmly on the floor. This position provides three points of contact with the floor and offers a better chance of surviving if they encounter a burnt through hole in the floor of the fire room compartment as they advance, because only one third of the body weight will be subjected to the risk of falling through. (See Photograph No 10)

This is also the best stance from which to apply the 'over pressure/under pressure' extinguishing techniques and perform a frontal attack advance (offensive mode) in complete sight and control of the flame front. This position is a compromise, because it limits the exposure to heat from the flame front above compared to being stood up and provides far more manoeuvrability than if you were lying or crawling on the floor.

51

An additional safety precaution is to have a security fire officer wearing breathing apparatus at the door of the fire room compartment with a back up branch/nozzle and radio communications as an integral part of a three person fire-fighting team, performing a co-ordinated attack in a secure, responsible, safe and offensive tactical mode.

The calorific value of the combustible fibreboards used in the Fire Development Simulators (FDS) is less than fire-fighters could encounter in a real fire involving polyurethane foam furniture. We do not routinely replicate the scenarios of polyurethane foam furniture burning in the simulators, which is another reason spotting/pulsating has been effective in simulated training scenarios and has lulled some compartment fire behaviour training (CFBT) Instructors into recommending its use on the fire ground.

There were similar circumstances arising from the early years of using converted steel freight containers as Fire Development Simulators (FDS) in Sweden in 1986. Recruit fire-fighters were arriving on fire stations in Sweden after attending the Fire Development Simulator (FDS) training and going into real fires with old hands (long serving fire-fighters) as partners in fire-fighting crews. The old hands were shocked to see these younger fire-fighters trying spotting/pulsating as they entered a fire room compartment, with a full flame front in the ceiling coming towards them at speed and about to be overrun, until the old hand stepped in, took over the branch/nozzle and applied the 'over pressure/under pressure' extinguishing technique and advanced to successfully control and extinguish the fire. The Fire Station Commanders soon got the message to the Swedish fire development training staff of the folly of believing in this myth and asked for them to emphasise to recruits the need to use the 'over pressure/under pressure' extinguishing techniques whilst fire-fighting at real fire incidents and refrain from reliance upon spotting/pulsing.

The Fire Development Simulator (FDS) – that I've personally designed and developed, as a result of years of research and dialogue with some of my good Swedish fire-fighting friends ☺ (Tore Eriksson, Marcus Dominques, Peter Norell, Nisse Bergstrom, Goran Cederholm, Mats Granat, Janne Karlsson and Hakan Brantas) for use at Manchester Airport Fire Service (MAFS) has the largest size top vent, that am currently aware of, in existence in the compartment fire behaviour training (CFBT) fire-fighting world. My friend Stephane Morizot ☺ (Lieutenant) - Saupeurs-Pompiers (Fire and Rescue Service) St Quentin, Yvelines, France has come closest to replicating my large size vent opening at their training ground in the suburbs of Paris and Stephane and his CFBT Instructors have done a tremendous job of introducing CFBT to the French Fire and Rescue Services and spreading the word, whilst simultaneously educating a culinary caveman like myself to the delights of French cuisine and wines during my interesting and wonderful visits to France.

The Fire Development Simulator (FDS) at the Manchester Airport Fire Service (MAFS) training ground with a large vent facilitates two metre wide flame fronts, which run the ceiling of the simulator to replicate reality during the training of the CFBT Instructors at MAFS. My advocacy of 'over pressure/ under pressure' extinguishing techniques fell on deaf ears at times because I could not get the flame front to run as fast as I knew it could in reality, by using fibreboards alone.

The day soon came when my brilliant and hard working CFBT Instructor Team at MAFS☺ Ian Roberts (Jack), Mick Kenny (Father Ted), Graham Ware, Mark Jones (Jonesy), Charlie Ellington, Peter Keefe, Martin Charlottes, Andrew Kipps and Nigel Kind (Snowie) decided to use discarded polyurethane foam airline seats from aircraft, having been made safe with the compressed air bolts being disarmed before use. They laid a row of seats below the flame front path and got to work as part of a CFBT instructors' personal development session, having completed the required risk assessment and with only qualified CFBT Instructors taking part.

The flame front eventually developed as planned but turned into an unexpected powerful force not previously encountered by the CFBT Instructors in the simulator. The flame front began to get the better of them, their normal extinguishing techniques were proving futile and they were about to fully open the vent and make a controlled withdrawal from this ever increasing forceful flame front. When, Jonesy said, "why not try, what 'John' has been on about all this time the 'over pressure/under pressure' extinguishing technique?" but a shorter more expletive version. Sure enough, the flame front shrank back like a genie going back into its bottle and they had complete control of the fire within seconds. The faster the flame front runs. The better and quicker these techniques will work because, as explained earlier, everything in nature tries to balance. As the 'over pressure' increases, physics redresses the balance by increasing the 'under pressure' and I know, now, that I have some truly converted disciples.

The free burning flames depicted in Photograph No.11, below, in my view is the definitive image of 'Over Pressure/Under Pressure' and clearly shows the flames exiting out of the top half of the doorway on 'over pressure' and air being sucked into the bottom half of the doorway on the 'under pressure' via the 'air track' towards the seat of the fire and beyond travelling through the exiting flame front.

Photograph No.11 - Flames exiting a doorway on 'over pressure'

To recap, imagine applying the 'over pressure/under pressure' extinguishing techniques to the flame front depicted in Photograph No 11 above, if it was inside a fire room compartment of a house/structure. How effective would they be on a flame front running this fast compared to the spotting/pulsing techniques and if you had the option, which of the two techniques would you use? Observe where and in what mode the fire-fighter is applying the water from the branch/nozzle to try to extinguish the fire.

The water is being applied in a straight stream format into the 'under pressure' region, which is contributing to forcing the flame front out of the doorway on 'over pressure'. If this were the chosen technique inside a fire room compartment the fire-fighters would be engulfed in a ball of fire.

In 1991 during an educational research visit to Sweden, I met Anders Lauren (The Baker), who explained how he came up with the brilliant concept of using converted steel freight containers as Fire Development Simulators (FDS), and then showed us practically that you could even extinguish the seat of the fire on the floor of the simulator (kindling fire-original open ignition source) and the flame front in the ceiling would continue to develop independently.

He also demonstrated safely and in a controlled manner the use of the straight stream format water application on the 'under pressure' region will truly force the flame front in the ceiling to come towards you and more importantly your facemask.

So, what would you achieve by using straight stream or spotting/pulsating as extinguishing techniques, if you were unfortunate enough as a fire-fighter to be confronted with high-energy combustible gases (smoke) burning in a powerful fast running flame front coming towards you in the ceiling, with a thick black smoke layer below it?

Or would using the 'over pressure/under pressure' extinguishing technique be a viable alternative. Obviously fire-fighters must train extensively to become competent in using the 'over pressure/under pressure' extinguishing techniques before being able to safely apply them on the fire-ground and this can only be achieved in a Fire Development Simulator (FDS) with a large controllable vent to replicate safely a free running fire in the ceiling of a fire room compartment.

CHAPTER FOUR

HOT SMOKE CONDITIONS

PART ONE

HOT "RICH" FLASHOVER

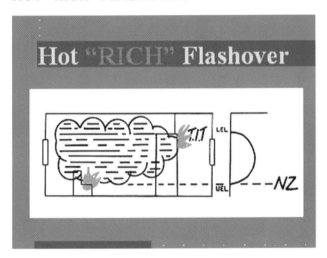

Figure No.19 – Hot 'Rich' Flashover

Hot Smoke Conditions inside the closed up fire room compartment.

This is the third type of flashover and called a **Hot 'RICH' Flashover** because the smoke/combustible gases inside the closed up fire room compartment are still at the smouldering/pulsating stage and have reached their thermal ignition temperature, which as described earlier, is when they have been progressively heated and the lower explosive limit has extended down the flammable range towards 0% fuel/air mixtures. In simple terms this means they have been heated by transfer of energy through the smoke layer whilst on the burn up, positive phase of the pulsation cycle.

Now the molecules of the smoke/combustible gases have rubbed together so much that all it needs to produce a flame instantaneously is the introduction of air, because without it, the flammable gas/air mixture inside the fire room compartment is too rich to burn except in the area adjacent to the ignition source. The smoke/combustible gases inside the fire room compartment are now hot and rich.

Then, when the door to the closed up fire room compartment is opened by either a member of the public or fire-fighters, the smoke/combustible gases will exit the fire room compartment on 'over pressure' and enter the corridor in the top half, instantaneously producing a flame on contact with air (creating an open ignition source) in the corridor.

Simultaneously air will enter the fire room compartment on 'under pressure' and follow the direction of the 'air track' in, down and around, up and out and begin to dilute the smoke/combustible gases exiting the fire room compartment, bringing them back down from being too rich to within their flammable range. With the open ignition source (flame) in the corridor, the flames can now travel backwards into the fire room compartment and flashover if left unabated! Hence, described as a hot 'rich' flashover.

If the hot smoke/combustible gases exiting the fire room compartment spontaneously ignite on contact with air in the corridor, after the fire-fighters have opened the door, because they are at their thermal ignition temperature, a fire-fighter might not be looking for this type of open ignition source above their head. This fire burning backwards into the room with the ensuing downward and sideways radiation does not make conditions any better inside the fire room compartment.

Additionally, if the grey smoke in the corridor outside the closed up fire room compartment is near its ideal mixture, is there any way of evaluating whether or not the smoke/combustible gases inside the fire room compartment are already at their thermal ignition temperature before fire-fighters open the door.

If not, why roll the dice and take a gamble, when the stakes are so high and risk creating a self induced explosion in the corridor.

Despite the guidance from the British Fire Service Manual[27] advising to ventilate by breaking the external window to the fire room compartment to alleviate a potential 'backdraft', if, presumably there are no persons reported inside.

How can the fire-fighters tell for sure if there is anyone inside the fire room compartment until they search it?

Breaking the external windows in this instance has the potential to create a free flaming full room fire and fire spread to other parts of the building and

---

[27] Fire Service Manual: Compartment Fires and Tactical Ventilation.
Volume 2, Fire Service Operations, HM Fire Service Inspectorate Publications Section, London: The Stationary Office (1997) Page 10.

possible fatal consequences for anyone inside if they were fortunate to be still alive. There have been many occasions upon arrival of the Fire Services/ Departments at fires that they have been reliably informed that there were no persons reported inside the house/structure involved in the fire, only to subsequently discover there were actually persons trapped inside, and persons have been subsequently found during the search and rescue operations.[28]

Remember everything is not always what it seems. Can you really take the chance to break that window, on hearsay, alone?

The conditions should not get any worse following the arrival of the Fire Service/Department at the fire-ground. In my view, we should not allow the fire to develop after we arrive, by inadvertently giving the rich flammable gas/ air mixture in the fire room compartment the air it needs to burn.

If fire-fighters could be shown how to get in the room without any flame-up, reconnoitre the room and depart safely with any casualties and no more burn damage, then, when they arrived, would they choose this to other methods? And if they could do this successfully would they class themselves as a very professional and extremely efficient effective fire fighting force, even though it means sacrificing the age old ritual of fighting the fire at close quarters. It may become boring beating the fire with our brain instead of our brawn, but we come back to the same old question:

WHY ARE THE FIRE-FIGHTERS ATTENDING THIS FIRE?

Is the priority to perform the task of rescue or fire-fighting?

---

[28] Clark, William E., "Fire-fighting Principles & Practices" 2nd edition (New York, 1990).Pages 112-113.

PART TWO

HOT "RICH" FLASHOVER/BACKDRAFT

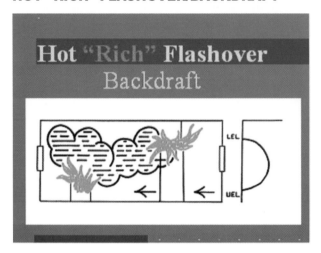

Figure No.20 – Hot 'Rich' Flashover/Backdraft

Another possible scenario can occur simultaneously with a hot 'rich' flashover; upon opening the door to the closed up fire room compartment, a 'backdraft' can occur from the smouldering open ignition source outward towards the door (exit port) because of the inflow of air on the 'air track'. What this means is that there will be two flame fronts, one travelling outward and the other inward at the same time, which will meet very quickly inside the room, increasing the flame-up and the full room fire stage will be reached very quickly.

If you have not got control of the door after opening it and a hot 'rich' flashover/ backdraft occurs, even a good fire-fighter would have difficulty in extinguishing these two flame fronts simultaneously, to prevent a full room fire. Not only the occupants and contents of the room could be lost, but also fire-fighters would struggle to prevent this powerful force of nature from spreading the fire to other parts of the building, causing the fire-fighters to retreat and regroup for another attack.

CHAPTER FIVE

COLD SMOKE CONDITIONS

PART ONE

'DELAYED FLASHOVER'

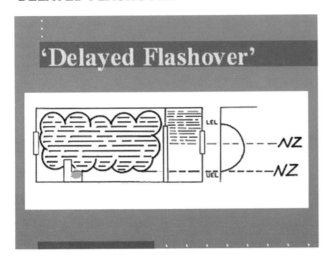

Figure No.21 – 'Delayed Flashover'

Cold Smoke Conditions in the corridor outside the closed up fire room compartment.

The **'Delayed Flashover'** is the fourth type of flashover.

It is called this because there is a delay before the flashover occurs. That is to say, the smoke (flammable gas/air mixture) is allowed to go past its lower explosive limit or come down from its upper explosive limit before an open ignition source is introduced, therefore there is a delay before ignition.

OR

When the flammable gas/air mixture inside a closed up fire room compartment has become so hot, that it is at its thermal ignition temperature and at 0% flammable gas/air mixture on the flammable range chart (See Figure No. 2), it will ignite on contact with air.

When the door to the closed up fire room compartment is opened, the smoke/

combustible gases will vacate the room into the upper half of the corridor on 'over pressure' and virtually instantaneously on contact with air in the upper half of the corridor, ignite and produce a flame – an open ignition source. This can subsequently ignite the flammable gas/air mixture in the corridor, which if near the ideal mixture can rapidly produce either a 'delayed flashover', or a 'fire gas explosion' in the corridor, with possible fatal consequences.

An example of a 'delayed flashover' is when the fire inside the closed up fire room compartment is at the smouldering/pulsating stage and the cold smoke/combustible gases (grey) in the corridor are progressively increasing in volume. They get more and more flammable with every pulsation and gradually approach their ideal mixture whilst simultaneously the smoke/combustible gases inside the closed up fire room compartment, progressing with each pulsation towards its thermal ignition temperature.

Suppose the smoke/combustible gases inside the closed up fire room compartment have reached their thermal ignition temperature, by the time the Fire Service/Department is summoned. The fire attack crew wearing breathing apparatus proceed down the corridor/hallway and do nothing to the cold grey smoke outside the closed up fire room compartment. They then open the door to the closed up fire room compartment and the cold grey smoke is near to its ideal mixture. The cold grey smoke has gone past its lower explosive limit some time ago, but when the door opens the black smoke comes out on 'over pressure' into the top half of the corridor, contacts the air and instantaneously produces a flame. This is the subsequent open ignition source for the cold grey smoke in the corridor - so there has been a delay before this ignition source has been introduced into the cold grey smoke near its ideal mixture.

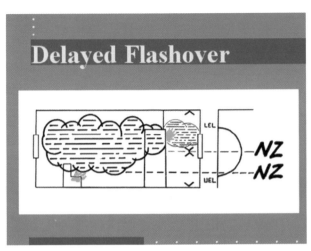

Figure No. 22 - Open Ignition Source for a 'Delayed Flashover' in the corridor

This flame (open ignition source) will now ignite the cold grey smoke layer. If it is near the ideal mixture at approximately a half way horizontal position in the corridor, it can expand on ignition to three to four times its volume and hit the floor and ceiling simultaneously then take the least line of resistance to the exit port of the corridor. It will choose to go away from the fire room compartment because of the 'over pressure' of the rich flammable gas/air mixture inside the fire room compartment and go out towards the less pressure resistant fresh air via the corridor. This will create an even bigger expansion in the corridor and, if the door to the fire room compartment is still open, will pull inwards the external glass window (suck it in) inside the fire room compartment, which is already weakened by the 'mechanism of fire'.

PART TWO

'FIRE GAS EXPLOSION'

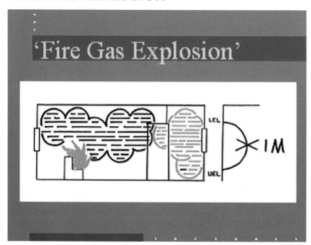

Figure No.23 – 'Fire Gas Explosion'

The fifth type of flashover is known as a **'Fire Gas Explosion'.**

This basically is when a 'delayed flashover' involving high-energy combustible gases (smoke) ignites exactly at the ideal mixture, which creates a 'fire gas explosion' at approximately half the force of methane, up to 8 bars pressure. This type of flashover will cause structural damage to the building/structure, which is a telltale sign during any later Fire Investigation. The subsequent damage can cause injury/death to fire-fighters from the resulting collapse of the building/structure, away from the original ignition source of the explosion.

A distinct difference between a 'delayed flashover' and in particular a 'fire gas explosion' and backdrafts/lean flashovers is that the resulting explosion will explode unilaterally and is less easily survived because of the speed and expansion. A backdraft /lean flashover is a progressive flame front from either the rich or lean side on the 'air track' and could go over your head, whereas an explosion is an expansion of a flame front equidistantly. A 'delayed flashover' or 'fire gas explosion' involving high-energy combustible gases (smoke) is one of the major contributing factors in causing serious and fatal injuries to fire-fighters all over the world.

We must begin to understand fire in its entirety to prevent these injuries to fire-fighters. Fire is predictable and with the correct knowledge, training, equipment and standard operating procedures (SOPs) we should not lose fire-fighters to

63

the powerful force of nature, fire, the only exception being human error on the part of a fire-fighter. The additional financial resources to provide the required knowledge, training, equipment and standard operating procedures (SOPs) should be made available as a gesture and an acknowledgement by society of the dangerous and difficult tasks fire-fighters perform in their role of protecting members of their communities from the devastating effects of fire.

We did not know before, because we thought fire was unpredictable. Now we know, we must act and implement the changes required to protect our fire-fighters.

> *"The dogmas of the quiet past are inadequate to the stormy present. The occasion is piled high with difficulty, and we must rise with the occasion. As our case is new, so we must think anew, and act anew"*[29]

President Lincoln's Second Annual Message to Congress, December 1, 1862.

However, these theories must be incorporated into the standard operating procedures (SOPs) if we are to achieve our objectives - the security of the fire-fighters, saving life and property.

All fires are predictable - if there is free flaming you can identify the air intake by using the clear indicators 'over' and 'under pressure'.

Photograph No.12. – Flames issuing from the bottom of the window sill upwards from an upper floor window

---

[29] http://home.att.net/~rjnorton/Lincoln78.html

'Size up', Photograph No. 12 above.

Where is the air feeding the fire entering this building/structure and are the door/doors to the fire room compartment open or closed?

Consider the impact of your diagnosis on your choice of tactics.

If the flame front has fully engulfed the window and 'over pressure' is forcing flames out from the bottom of the window sill upwards and the whole opening is showing flames the 'under pressure' air supply has to be below the level of the bottom of the window sill. Hence the air entering the fire room compartment must be below the window sill level and could only be coming from the open doorway to the fire room compartment and from a subsequently open external door to fresh air at ground floor level (UK) below the position of the window sill.

Another, simple analogy was given to me by a policeman at a fire, which perfectly explains flame travel in layman's terms. He said "The flames coming out of the window looked like water pouring out of the window upside down". When, you think about it, this makes perfect sense because water will always try to find the lowest point, being heavier than air, and flames/smoke will always strive for the highest point being warm and buoyant and travel upwards on 'over pressure', being lighter than air.

These new found diagonostic skills will tell you a lot about the stage of the fire but will not negate the need to reconnoitre around the back of the building to check if any persons require rescuing from upper floor windows by ladder etc.

Where there is no flame-up and the fire is bottled up, with black smoke in the fire room compartment, the only real difference is the size of the fire room compartment containing the fuel (black smoke)[30]. Once you hit the black smoke, that is the extent of the rich mixture and if we control the 'air flows' how can it burn up?

Why let air get to it?

---

[30] In the case histories section of our website **www.smokeburns.com** I shall expand on this concept and provide explanations of how in my view it is feasible for flames to be showing from the top half of a kitchen window at the rear of the house/structure on the ground floor (UK) and the remainder of two storey house/structure can be fully charged with black smoke, which is emitting black smoke, but no flames from the front first floor (UK) bedroom window because all the external doors are closed and all the internal doors are open, effectively making this two storey structure one large single fire compartment.

CHAPTER SIX

'The Rule of Five'

Learn to 'Read the Fire Gases'.

Nature has given us five signs, which will assist fire-fighters to diagnose what stage the fire inside and outside the closed up fire room compartment is at between A – Z of the 'mechanism of fire' and predict and protect against its flammable and explosive potential.

The five signs of the fire gases are:

1. **M**ovement
2. **I**gnitability
3. **T**emperature
4. **C**olour
5. **H**orizontal position of the neutral zone (NZ)

To remember these signs try using the acronym **'MITCH'.**

Fire-fighters should develop skills to read these five signs, because;

'The rule of five' will keep you alive.

I am reliably informed that the use of the phrase **'The rule of five'** is a defined as 'terms of art' and I chose the definition in a similar vein to 'The rule of thumb', because having five digits on our hands and in the heat of battle I would personally find it very useful to remind myself of the five things am looking for by using the acronym **MITCH** and counting them out on one hand, whilst 'sizing-up' the fire am attending.

I'll try to explain these 'terms of art' and the importance of each sign and the logic behind their relevance to fire development:

1. Movement

The movement of the fire gases (smoke layer) is a clear indication of the effect the 'air flows' are having on the smoke layer. A static cold black smoke layer indicates that the smoke layer has become detached from the original ignition source in the fire room compartment. A static grey smoke layer indicates seepage from the closed up fire room compartment and both scenarios denote that the air flows are not causing the flames at the seat of the fire to burn up through the smoke layer because they are either detached or isolated by a closed door.

Pulsating black smoke emitting on 'over pressure' from an exit port (window/door) of a fire room compartment indicates that air is getting to the seat of the fire, but there is some back pressure in the smoke layer, creating the illusion of the smoke pulsating, following the overcoming of the back pressure the next visible sign will be the pulsations getting less and less and then a flame front reaching the exit port.

The introduction of the concept of **'The rule of five'** and the above explanations are only the beginning of applying this style of diagnostic approach, which will in my view, enable fire-fighters to develop the required **'size-up'** skills to be able to **'read the fire gases'** and establish which stage the fire is at upon arrival and predict what can happen and if you are able to get control of the 'air flows' to this fire, you should be able dictate what is going to occur and be in charge of this fire.

2. Ignitability

The fire gases showing may have already ignited prior to arrival and are free flaming from an exit port (window/door) which confirms their ignitability and can be dealt with successfully by the application of the 'under pressure' extinguishing technique as described in Chapter Three, Part Two.

The colour and horizontal position of the neutral zone (NZ) are good indicators of the ignitability of the fire gases and are covered below.

The ignitability of fire gases bottled up inside a fire room compartment can be assessed by observing the fire gases exiting on 'over pressure' from the fire room compartment, upon opening of the door to see if they ignite on contact with air in the corridor, indicating whether they are at the thermal ignition temperature or not, following implementation of the relevant safety steps, explained in Chapter Seven below, prior to opening up the fire room compartment.

3. Temperature

The temperature of the fire gases is a big indicator of their fire development and explosive potential.

The fire gases exiting are normally either warm/hot or relatively cold.

If the fire gases are warm/hot upon opening up the fire room compartment, then it is safe to assume the air intake, now entering via the open doorway is getting to the seat of the fire on the 'air track' and burning up through the flame front towards the exit port were the fire-fighters are positioned 'reading the fire gases'.

Conversely, if the fire gases are relatively cold then you can diagnosis that if they are grey and static smoke in a corridor, this is because of seepage from the adjacent fire room compartment. However, if the fire gases are black cold smoke emitting approximately 450mm (18") above the floor level from a closed up fire room compartment following the opening of the door and they have very little movement, this indicates that there is no flame–up at the seat of the fire and the fire gases are travelling away from the ignition source and the two are becoming detached from each other.

4. Colour

The colour of the smoke indicates the comparative amount of fuel and air that these fire gases actually contain, basically grey smoke denotes more air than fuel and indicates a lean mixture possibly moving towards its ideal mixture on the flammable range.

Black smoke denotes more fuel than air and is more likely to above its upper explosive limit and indicates a rich mixture that is oxygen deficient.

White smoke (steam) denotes the evaporation moisture contained within combustible materials e.g. white smoke emitting from a shingle tiled roof is indicating flames are impinging on the roof tiles either externally or internally and the next thing to show following the total evaporation of the moisture will be high energy fire gases (black smoke) that may subsequently ignite and involve the entire roof space.

5. Horizontal position of the neutral zone (NZ)

The horizontal position of the neutral zone (NZ) gives a visual indication of the position of the fire gases (smoke layer) on the inverted flammable range chart (See Figure No. 6) and if there is a black smoke layer inside a closed up fire room compartment approximately 450mm (18") above the floor level this indicates a rich mixture above its upper explosive limit.

A cold black static smoke layer in a halfway horizontal position inside a fire room compartment following the opening up of the compartment indicates the neutral zone (NZ) is in the vicinity of its ideal mixture and most likely will contain high-energy combustible gases and these circumstances can be diagnosed to indicate the realistic possibility of a 'cold smoke explosion'.

A cold grey static smoke layer in a halfway horizontal position in a corridor outside a closed up fire room compartment indicates that the neutral zone (NZ) could be some where between the lower explosive limit and its ideal mixture and within its flammable range.

A warm grey smoke layer moving with force, exiting the building/structure on 'over pressure' indicates the air intake is getting to the seat of the fire, but the 'lean flashover' stage may not have yet been reached in the ceiling area above the seat of the fire, because of the open plan nature of the building/structure.

The free flaming stage gives a clear indication of the air intake and as previously discussed fire-fighters need to develop their 'size-up' skills to identify the horizontal position of the neutral zone (NZ) in the flame front and the 'under pressure' region and then they have the option of applying the 'under pressure' extinguishing technique from the exterior.

CHAPTER SEVEN

Standard Operating Procedures (SOP's)

Search and Rescue

PART ONE – HOT SMOKE CONDITIONS

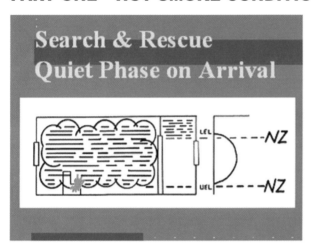

Figure No.24 – Search and Rescue

We will now try to apply - **The 'Rule of Five'** to the following scenario. Hot smoke conditions inside a closed up fire room compartment on the ground floor (UK) of a single storey house/structure with persons trapped inside the room and they require rescuing (See Figure No. 24) above. To assist the diagnostic approach I've designed steps to deal with the various ways in which the fire could develop.

STEP 1 – 'Size up'

Upon arrival the Fire Service/Department finds the corridor/hallway has grey smoke (lean) approximately halfway down from the ceiling. As you open the front door to the building you see there is a cold grey smoke layer (lean) in a halfway horizontal position and there is no movement just lazy, stratifying grey smoke.

Is the door to the closed up fire room compartment open or shut?

The fire room compartment door is closed, because as you opened the front door and allowed air to flow freely into the building/structure, it did not disturb the smoke movement and you can see lazy cold grey smoke in the corridor, confirming air cannot be getting to the seat of the fire. The diagnostic process has begun: we have a single fire room compartment, full of fuel (black smoke). The first consideration is to remove the fuel outside the closed up fire room compartment and secure around the fire, before we consider our next option.

You locate the closed up fire room compartment by feeling the heat transmitting through the door with the back of your hand and evaluating the pulsating smoke emitting around the gaps. Conformation can also be received from fire-fighting crews during reconnoitre of the building that the fire room compartment is full of black smoke (rich) and the window is still closed and intact.

What would you do next? Adopt a traditional approach and ventilate from the exterior by breaking the window from outside or embrace the 'New Order' and try another way that will not result in a full room fire.

The principle of this 'New Order' is that the security of the fire-fighters is of paramount importance.

STEP 2 – Secure around the fire. (Ventilation)

VENTILATION

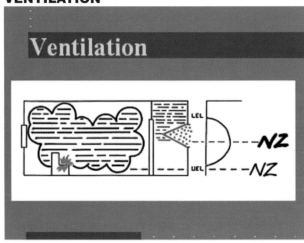

Figure No.25 – Water Fogging Ventilation Technique

Secure around the fire before you open the closed up fire room compartment.

Ventilate the Cold Grey Smoke

If the configuration of the building/structure allows you (See Figure No.25), remove the flammable/explosive risk outside the fire room compartment by opening the window in the corridor and use the water fogging ventilation technique (the 'venturri' principle).[31] Point your water spray branch/nozzle outwardly, just inside the window opening, creating a positive pressure outside and an area of low pressure behind it and like a tube train leaving an underground station air rushes into equalise the difference ☺ [32]. The newly created negative pressure in the corridor allows the cold grey smoke to vacate the exit port by being sucked to the outside. Alternatively, a positive pressure ventilation (PPV) fan, if available, can be turned on at the front door with all the openings shut except the desired entry point (front door) and exit port (corridor window) and ventilate the grey smoke. Once this is achieved, the positive pressure ventilation (PPV) fan should be re-positioned to blow air away from the hallway (entry point) and left idling ready for further use if required.

STEP 3 - 'Inertia of the Grey Smoke'

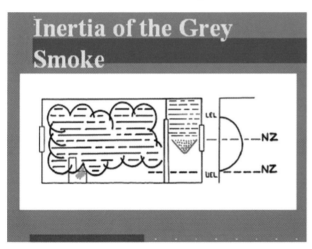

Figure No.26 – Inertia of the Grey Smoke in the corridor

---

[31] www.allstar.fiu.edu/aerojava/pic3-2.htm
[32] Analogy provided by Linda Elizabeth Rice for the 'Under Fire' TV programme by my wonderful wife.(July 1995).

72

Inertia of the Grey Smoke

If the configuration of the building/structure will not easily allow ventilation of the grey smoke (fire gases) in the corridor outside the closed up fire room compartment without a considerable time delay, an alternative is to cool the grey smoke (See Figure No. 26), and in so doing, shrink the flammable range of the combustible gases in the corridor. This will reduce their flammability by inertia. The British Fire Service Manual[33], now acknowledges that 'smoke burns' and this is a valid system of work to make this flammable gas cloud safer - a massive step forward from the days of one paragraph describing flashover and doubts from some British Fire Officers on the relevance and need to cool this grey smoke, due to the relative infrequency of flashovers, in their opinion. Some scientific comments state that some of the smoke doesn't burn, so we can't say, that 'smoke burns'.

My response, to these observations was to state that British Fire Service Manuals are not scientific documents and in fact the compartment fire behaviour training (CFBT) manuals are for fire-fighters, not scientists.

We are able to safely apply water spray droplets into a cold grey smoke layer in a corridor outside a closed up fire room compartment to create the desired inertia, because any turbulence created will not disturb the ignition source inside the closed up fire room compartment, because the door is closed, which prevents the air reaching the seat of the fire.

---

[33] Fire Service Manual: Compartment Fires and Tactical Ventilation.
Volume 2, Fire Service Operations, HM Fire Service Inspectorate Publications Section, London: The Stationary Office (1997) Page 21.

STEP 4 - 'Water Vapour Barrier'

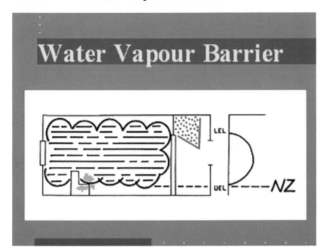

Figure No.27 – Water Vapour Barrier

Create a water vapour barrier

Once you have secured around the fire and removed or made the flammable/ explosive risk inert, you must create a water vapour barrier in the area adjacent to the closed up fire room compartment door, above the door and on the adjacent ceiling, by spraying water droplets on this area. Upon opening the door to the closed up fire room compartment, either warm/hot black smoke or cold black smoke will exit on 'over pressure' and will either ignite on contact with air or they will not. If they do ignite on contact with air in the corridor, this will produce a flame because the fire gases are at their thermal ignition temperature. The linings in the upper half of the corridor could now decompose because of the flame impingement and feed the flames.

However, if water spray droplets are applied to this area, then on the production of a flame, this will generate enough heat to create a water vapour barrier upon the application of heat and prevent the decomposition of the linings, whilst fire-fighters reinstate the status quo by closing the door to the fire room compartment and in so doing buying valuable thinking time and maintaining control of the air flows.

STEP 5 – Reading the fire gases inside the fire room compartment.

The fire gases exiting on 'over pressure' will either be warm/hot or cold and if, the black smoke exiting is warm/hot and igniting on contact with air in the corridor, this is a clear indication that a hot 'rich' flashover is about to take hold and burn backwards into the fire room compartment and even if the warm/hot black smoke emitting does not ignite on contact with air in the corridor, there is still the realistic possibility of a 'backdraft' occurring inside the fire room compartment.

Therefore, if fire-fighters encounter warm/hot black smoke approximately 450mm (18") above the floor level of the fire room compartment (horizontal position of the neutral zone) exiting on 'over pressure' with forceful movement and either igniting on contact with air in the corridor or not.

How many of the signs of **The 'Rule of Five' (MITCH)** can be recognised and their significance diagnosed to enable fire-fighters to make an informed decision on how to apply the correct tactics to deal with these 'hot' smoke conditions inside a closed up fire room compartment?

How would you proceed to tackle these 'hot' smoke conditions inside a closed up fire room compartment?

Fight your way in and leave the door open to provide an exit route or would you consider cooling the fire gases enough to ensure they stay below their thermal ignition temperature and then enter the room with your branch/nozzle and enough hose to search the room and close the door behind you onto the hose, which should keep the flammable gas/air mixture inside the fire room compartment 'rich'?

We can now proceed to implement Step 5.1 below and find out my preferred option:

STEP 5.1 – Reduce the temperature below the thermal ignition temperature (TIT).

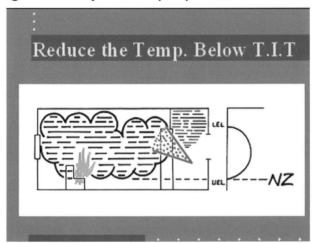

Figure No.28. - Reduce the temperature below the thermal ignition temperature (T.I.T.)

To safely enter the fire room compartment to perform the rescue, fire-fighters should ensure they prevent either a hot 'rich' flashover burning back into the room or a 'backdraft' burning up from inside the room or both occurring simultaneously.

To achieve this, we open the door slightly and maintain control of the 'air flows'. As the black smoke comes out, we insert water spray droplets into the upper half of the fire room compartment from the doorway (See Figure No. 28), then pull the water spray branch/nozzle out and allow the water spray to mix for 10 -15 seconds then, continue to repeat this process until the hot black smoke does **not** ignite on contact with air and we have now reduced the hot black smoke exiting the fire room compartment below its thermal ignition temperature.

Before I explain the entry procedure into the fire room compartment, I must comment on another tactic that has become prevalent in the UK during the introduction of compartment fire behaviour training (CFBT). The door entry technique of wetting the door leading into the closed up fire room compartment prior to entry, to establish the horizontal position of the neutral zone (NZ) inside the closed up fire room compartment in my view is flawed. This technique is effective during training in the Fire Development Simulators (FDS) because the majority of these have metal doors, which get a lot warmer than the wooden doors fitted in most domestic dwellings.

The horizontal position of the neutral zone (NZ) can be easily established by simply opening the door to the fire room compartment in a controlled manner. My real concern is that when water is applied to a very hot wooden door it can cause shrinkage and if the gap before application of the water was less than 5mm[34], then any flames inside the fire room compartment impinging on an aperture smaller than 5mm are cooled sufficiently to prevent them penetrating through the gap. However, if the shrinkage caused by the application of water creates a gap bigger than 5mm, then flames may be able to penetrate through the door and into the adjacent corridor and if, the fire-fighters using this technique have not secured around the fire properly by ventilating or inertia of the grey smoke layer in the corridor outside the fire room compartment and the grey smoke is near its ideal mixture, the inadvertent release of a flame from inside the fire room compartment caused by shrinking the door could result in the fire-fighters being engulfed in a 'delayed flashover' or, worse still, a 'fire gas explosion'. I feel the benefits gained from the above technique do not outweigh the faint but realistic possibility of fire-fighters being caught out and engulfed by a fireball.

STEP 6 – Entry Procedure

At this point, the fire attack crew, consisting of two members wearing breathing apparatus and equipped with a 'Blaster' style high-pressure branch/nozzle and hose reel tubing[35] (30 litres per minute and 19mm diameter) enter the room, with water at the ready via the door, throw in the hose reel tubing (sufficient to search the room) and step to one side to avoid any possible flame front from a 'backdraft'. The team should also consist of a Security Officer (Junior Officer - Crew Commander UK), wearing breathing apparatus and equipped with radio communication facility to the fire attack team and a backup 'Fogfighter' style low pressure branch/nozzle and hose (300/450 litres per minute and 45mm diameter). The Security Officer takes control of the door (air flows) and closes the door on to the hose reel tubing.

Why, do this, when, all our Fire Service careers we have had it ingrained into us to secure the route out of the building/structure to facilitate a safe retreat?

The fire attack crew have taken the opportunity to enter during a natural pause created by reducing the temperature (See Step 5.1), when the hot black smoke

---

[34] British Standards BS 8214: 1990. 'Fire door assemblies with non-metallic leaves' Page 19 Section 13.4.

[35] Fire Departments/Services who do not use high pressure hose reel branch/nozzles and tubing can perform this entry technique with normal low pressure branch/nozzles and hose that can provide the required maximum 0.3mm size water droplets e.g. 'Fogfighter' style branch and hose (300/450 litres per minute and 45mm diameter).

exiting is not at its thermal ignition temperature because of the inertia created before entry. If the door had remained open, the 'air flow' could overtake the inertia and cause a hot 'rich' flashover. With the door remaining open there is the additional danger of a 'backdraft', which may come slightly later if the fire room compartment is L shaped and the smouldering fire (closed/concealed ignition source) is around the corner. As with the candle (See Photograph Nos. 8a, 8b, 8c & 8d), if we restrict the air the hot black smoke cannot burn, because the rich mixture is absorbing the energy required for the decomposition and combustion process. If we close the door onto the hose reel tubing this also restricts the hot black smoke exiting on 'over pressure' and the amount of air entering on the 'under pressure', thereby maintaining a balanced rich mixture inside the fire room compartment and reducing the possibility of the a burn up, unless an external window fails.

Now, your fire attack crew is inside a flammable mixture in a confined fire room compartment. Where is the risk? At any moment the fire attack crew inside the room could be faced with failure of an external window, which could result in a hot 'rich' flashover or 'backdraft' or both simultaneously and having to adopt an 'offensive mode' and use the 'over pressure' extinguishing technique. If the external window failed because of the effects of pressure when the door was virtually closed, the flame front would not go towards the door but to the newly created exit port at the external window. With the window being quite a small opening, it will be relatively some time; compared to full 'air flow' from an open door, before the back pressures are overcome and we reach the 'full room fire' stage.

So, immediately upon failure of the window, the fire attack crew inside the fire room compartment go straight on into an 'offensive mode' to control and extinguish the developing flame front before it really takes a hold, by inserting water spray droplets into the 'over pressure' region and forcing the flame front and fire gases (smoke) towards and out of the window (exit port), achievable and safe because the door is closed too and all the flames, fire gases and steam will exit via the window, whilst simultaneously prohibiting air entering through the failed window. This 'offensive mode' is a variation of the water fogging ventilation techniques used in Step 2 (See Figure 25), but with the water spray branch/nozzle being further away from the actual failed window. The Security Officer is at the door of the fire room compartment with radio communications and a back up 300/450 litres per minute full water spray 'Fogfighter' style branch/nozzle to assist if required and to control the door for the subsequent ventilation of the inert fire gases and steam following extinguishment of the fire.

Personally I'd rather deal with a partially inert 'backdraft' inside the fire room compartment with the door closed by going straight to an 'offensive mode' and use of the 'over pressure' extinguishing technique, than having to deal with the scenario of the door being open and the 'backdraft' coming straight towards me and the remainder of the building possibly becoming involved.

If control is lost, what will happen to any casualties thus far not located in the other parts of the building/structure?

STEP 7 – Creating the 'SAUNA EFFECT'

Another security measure practised by the fire attack crew, once inside the fire room compartment, would be to begin inertia of the hot black smoke immediately upon entry, by putting two thirds of the water spray droplets into the black smoke and one third, onto the wall/ceiling linings of the room as they proceed to search the room. This ratio is hard to evaluate in dark, hot and humid conditions. So the 'rule of thumb' is to apply water spray droplets into the hot black smoke and on to the linings until you feel the steam inside your fire tunic and it has become like a sauna. (Steam/water vapour will find its way inside any personal protective clothing, except gas tight chemical suits).

Then you continue, and as the 'sauna effect' wears off, you re-apply some more water spray droplets to further reduce the flammability of the hot black smoke. By creating progressive inertia, you are tipping the scales of probability in your favour all the time and if you have reduced the effects of any subsequent fire development, then you are in a better position to immediately revert to an 'offensive mode' if the external window does fail. You can chase the residual flames, if any, out towards the failed external window, creating a safer working environment for the fire-fighters.

STEP 8 – Painting the wall linings

Next, the fire-fighters begin to cool the wall linings adjacent to the seat of the fire by turning the setting of the branch/nozzle to a straight stream (only slightly open) and gently wetting the linings, as if you were painting the walls with water instead of paint. This reduces the decomposition from the warmed up combustible linings inside the fire room compartment.

STEP 9 – Turning Over/Overhaul procedures

Then fire-fighters having located the original smouldering material (concealed/closed ignition source) at floor level, begin dampening down the seat of the fire with a small straight stream of water.

STEP 10 – Ventilating from inside the fire room compartment

Finally, the inert fire gases and steam require ventilating from the fire room compartment which can be achieved from inside by the fire-fighters opening or breaking the external window and using water fogging ventilation techniques (See Step 2 & Figure No.25).

Then, turning over/overhaul operations can commence. Now, that this particular type of fire incident has been safely dealt with, without flames having really seeing the light of day and any casualties, contents and the fabric of the building/structure have not deteriorated following the arrival of the Fire Service/Department, because the fire-fighters have taken full control of the fire development.

However, contrary to traditional concepts, the only disadvantage with these standard operational procedures (SOPs) is that, once inside of the fire room compartment with door closed behind you it is a hotter environment to work in, than if the flames were running along the ceiling, because the room is closed up and the heat is retained inside the room, conversely, when flames are exiting on 'over pressure', cold air is passing over the fire-fighters down at low level on 'under pressure' via the 'air track', making the conditions more bearable to work in. This surprises most people. So, how do you overcome this hostile environment you are now being asked to work in by using these new standard operational procedures (SOPs)?

Firstly, fire-fighters must train in the Fire Development Simulator (FDS) to see with your own eyes that the theory is correct – 'smoke burns'. Then, they must gain confidence in the use of your water spray branch/nozzle (e.g. 'Blaster' or 'Fogfighter' style branch/nozzle) and know it will perform in real fire conditions and they must also gain confidence in their personal protective equipment (PPE), which should include an 'over-hood' attached to the fire tunic in addition to a flash hood under your breathing apparatus facemask.

We must insulate our heads especially when advocating these standard operating procedures (SOPs), which encapsulate you in a combustible gas cloud, inside a fire room compartment. At present we insist on insulated over-trousers. If we protect our backsides, why don't we protect our heads, which are operating in higher temperatures than the rest of our body being at the highest point and nearest to any flame fronts running the ceiling?

Secondly, once inside the fire room compartment fire-fighters are carrying their onboard computer inside their heads. What do you think happens to the fluids inside your brain as they heat up in a fire? They expand. The most important part of your body to protect is your head. If your onboard computer fails or goes down you are out of the game. So, the introduction of universal over-hoods onto fire tunics is a **must** to perform these standard operational procedures (SOPs) safely.

Quality waterproof fire-fighting gloves are also essential for fire-fighters to be able to successfully perform these standard operating procedures (SOPs). During 17 years of Fire Development Simulator (FDS) training, the best performing pair of gloves I've used and most suitable for the task outlined in these standard operational procedures (SOPs), in my opinion, are the HUHTA (Finnish)[36] fire-fighting gloves. Others I've used have allowed excessive heat and/or water to penetrate through the gloves during fire-fighting training and operations.

I also discovered that leather fire boots were preferable for use in such high temperature working conditions. The concept of providing suitable protective clothing (personal protective equipment) for fire-fighters is to give them confidence in the use of their fire-fighting turnout gear and afford the correct level of protection. So, they can tolerate the temperatures and be comfortable in the knowledge that they and their fire-fighting branch/nozzle (weapon) can perform safely and effectively in this extremely hostile environment.

Now, that they know they can survive, instead of worrying about their own well-being, they can 'get to work'.

The fire-fighter must, also attain a certain level of heat tolerance to perform these standard operating procedures (SOPs) successfully. This is achieved during training in the Fire Development Simulator (FDS). The fire-fighter is re-committed to extinguish a flame front, ten metres (thirty foot) long on a repeat cycle, having already proved their competence in using the 'over pressure/ under pressure' extinguishing techniques. They are repeatedly re-committed into the Fire Development Simulator (FDS) until they reach their own limits of heat stress and are verging on their heat tolerance limits. When training in Sweden in 1991. I was subjected to this type of training and for the first time ever in my Fire Service career, eventually I said I'd had enough and could not go into the Fire Development Simulator (FDS), any more. I was spent. I was praised for this action but did not feel that I would have been, back home in the UK, feeling it would have been a sign of weakness to admit my limitations. I would have pressed on regardless, and because of the 'macho' image prevalent at that time and become a liability. Instead, in Sweden I learned that the bravest and safest course of action was to fight the fire with my brain and not just my brawn and call "time out" in the secure knowledge that the next fire-fighter would take over and finish the job off.

---

[36] The "Huhta" fire-fighting glove, OY B HUHTA AB, Kvranvagen 6, FIN – 68500 KRONOBY, Finland.

There are other important issues relevant to the realisation of one's limits:

"A smoke diver (fire-fighter wearing breathing apparatus) who carries out a physically demanding incursion into a really hot environment for 30-40 minutes will experience a reduction in his capacity to work as a result of heat stress, fluid loss, lactic acid build-up and insufficient sugar supply. Taking everything into consideration, it is totally realistic to assume that under these conditions a smoke diver may lose up to 75% of their capacity to work". [37]

The Swedish Fire and Rescue Services describe fire-fighting in breathing apparatus as smoke diving, in the same vein as underwater scuba diving and the smoke diving publication is one of the best breathing apparatus reference books I've ever read and only wish, that it had been available for perusal and study in 1978 during my initial breathing apparatus course, because it explains brilliantly the relevant aspects of usage whilst fire-fighting and I'd strongly recommend any operational fire-fighter to read it and learn from this simplistic and very informative publication.

Why train fire-fighters to find their limits when, the standard operational procedures (SOPs) are designed to avoid having to fight the fire by keeping it rich.

The repeated exposure to this flame front and finding your limits, also prepares you as a fire-fighter to face the most likely worse case scenarios. The trained fire-fighter can go straight to 'offensive mode', if whilst inside a fire room compartment performing search and rescue operations with the door closed to keep the fuel/air mixture rich, as described earlier (See Step 6) and an external window in the room fails, fire-fighters know they will be capable of forcing the fire gases and flames, out of the failed window by putting a water spray fog directly into the 'over pressure' region, towards the failed window. Because they have already been there, seen that, done it and got the tee shirt.

If you have done it once, you can do it again.

Talking of tee-shirts it was made clear to me that the use of man made fibres for undergarments (tee-shirts and trousers) worn beneath fire tunics was not advisable whilst working in such high temperatures, because of the possibility that they could melt and stick to the fire-fighters skin and undergarments made

---

[37] Malmsten, C & Rosander, M. "Smoke diving and other tasks with breathing apparatus" The National Board of Occupational Safety and Health, (Sweden, 1987) Giro-brand ab. Page 47.

from natural fibres would be preferable. The layering of these undergarments was also advisable and the way forward to provide additional insulation protection from the heat by creating pockets of air in between the layered clothing. Additionally, wearing of a long sleeved garment over a tee shirt was also desirable to protect your lower arms and thumb loops on the sleeves of fire tunics are a necessity to facilitate drawing down the fire tunic sleeves under the fire-fighting gloves, all of which ensures that no part of the fire-fighters skin is exposed during fire-fighting operational procedures. Another useful tip I acquired from Sweden was not to tighten up breathing apparatus set shoulder straps, because if you do the heat will impinge on the tightened straps and transmit straight through the undergarments onto your skin and possibly burn your shoulders, instead leave them looser and every so often shrug your shoulders to circulate the air underneath the straps to prevent heat accumulation.

PART TWO – The Final Frontier

You'd think we have now reached the 'Final Frontier' on dealing with closed up single fire room compartments. But, remember things are not always as they seem. ☺ [38]

---

[38] Whilst serving as fire-fighters on our beloved Red Watch E55 Stalybridge, Greater Manchester County (GMC) Fire Service (1977-84), myself and Les Kenworthy (Rambo), use to ride to work on our bicycles from our homes in Woodley. We had to go through a town called Hyde and we constantly disagreed about which was the quickest route through Hyde, the top or bottom road. So one day things came to a head and I bet Les I could beat him to work by taking my preferred lower road. Les was a former member of Her Majesty's Armed Forces and prided himself on his fitness. I knew he would beat me, but it was worth it to stop him arguing and he'd have to work up a sweat to prove it. As I meandered along the lower road and crossed over a motorway bridge, who should come along in his council flat bed lorry, but my father-in-law, Bill, on his way to the clearance site of a large fire, which we actually attended in Stalybridge (Chemstar). Bill pulled over and said "throw your bike in the back, John and I'll give you a lift to work". What a result!

I arrived at the fire station well before Les and proceeded to hide my bike away from our usual parking space, had a shower got changed into my undress uniform ready for parade and then got a mug of tea and waited for Les to come steaming into the yard like a young Lance Armstrong. I watched discreetly from a window out of sight to observe Les's beaming face, upon realising that my bike had not yet arrived. That was my cue, I went to my open locker and as Les entered the locker room I pulled from my locker a mug of tea and in full undress uniform asked him, "where have you been?" His face said a thousand words, but the rest of him was dumbfounded and he spent the whole day likewise, with all the other members of Red Watch aware of the ruse…happy days. I finally told Les the story, after work over a beer and am not sure if he was relieved or aggrieved. Maybe it was antics like this that contributed to our fun loving and life-long friendship.

By the way, Les if you are reading this you still owe me that fiver from the bet.

Compartment Fire Behaviour Training (CFBT)

To safely implement the standard operational procedures (SOPs) from Step 6 – 10, inclusive, as outlined above. I do recognise that high levels of heat tolerance are required for entry into the fire room compartment at the hot 'rich' flashover/backdraft stage and after making the fire gases inert and performing search and rescue operations in this hot environment of black smoke enclosed in the fire room compartment with the door closed onto the hose lines. These SOPs can only be achieved by facilitating intensive fire development simulation training and ensuring fire-fighters are deemed competent by qualified CFBT staff.[39]

Therefore, after 17 years' researching fire development in many countries, my conclusion is that the practicalities of implementing intensive Fire Development Simulator (FDS) training may prove to be logistically prohibitive for the existing operational personnel in Fire Brigades/Departments with large numbers of fire-fighters. However, this training is imperative to achieve the desired heat tolerance to perform these standard operational procedures (SOPs) Steps 6 – 10 (inclusive). But, before we discuss the '"Taylor-Made" Solution' as an alternative, it is imperative that fire-fighters who are dealing with a closed up fire room compartment, full of black smoke (rich), and following securing around the fire by ventilation or inertia and creation of a water vapour barrier (Step 3 & 4) recognise the need to 'read the fire gases' inside the fire room compartment on all occasions, (Step 5) and not only to establish if the fire gases exiting on 'over pressure' will ignite on contact with air, but most importantly to assess if the black smoke exiting the fire room compartment is either 'hot' or 'cold', because if the black smoke is **cold** then you **cannot** use the '"Taylor-Made" Solution'.

Admittedly, new personnel can be trained in a structured way from recruitment, but we need a short-term solution and I feel the one I am now going to propose will meet the identified training need. It is a compromise and an amalgamation of various good practices I've observed throughout the world of fire-fighting.

---

[39] The British Fire Service in conjunction with our awarding body for competence based training - Edexcel are currently developing the Compartment Fire Behaviour Training (CFBT) Instructors knowledge and understanding award and certificate (BTEC) to ensure that instructors are trained in CFBT and Positive Pressure Ventilation (PPV) techniques to a nationally recognised standard, that is externally quality assured by Edexcel. The award consists of two CFBT units and an additional unit for PPV techniques which will merit a certificate. I had the honour and privilege of being the author of two of the units and my colleague – Paul Cross from the Devon Fire and Rescue Service wrote the other unit. I'd also like to thank Neil Withers of the London Fire and Emergency Planning Authority and all my colleagues on the Chief Fire Officer's Association CFOA (UK) CFBT National Practitioners' Group for their support and guidance and Moira Hargreaves, Sukhvinder Bhatnager, Rachel Hendrick and James Haskins from Edexcel for their academic guidance in developing the award and certificate, scheduled to be available in 2007.

The "Taylor-Made" Solution

So, what if after 'reading the fire gases' inside the closed up fire room compartment (Step 5) the black smoke exiting is 'hot'.

Now, is the opportunity to apply the '"Taylor-Made" Solution' and introduce the alternative to Step 5.1 by replacing it with Step 5.2 and inert the closed up fire room compartment remotely from the corridor, it is exactly the same principle as used by fire-fighters years ago at basement fires, they use to make a hole in the floor above a basement fire and then insert a basement branch/nozzle through the hole and began inertia of the basement with water spray droplets to extinguish the fire and sufficiently cool the environment to enable a fire attack breathing apparatus crew to enter the basement to finish the job off and begin turning over/overhaul procedures.

Step 5.2 - Inertia using a 'Mitre' style piercing branch/nozzle from the corridor outside the closed up fire room compartment.

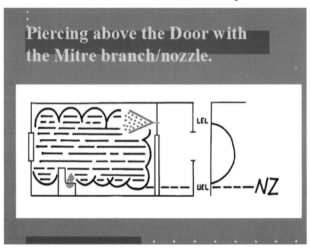

Figure No.29 – Inertia from the corridor outside the closed up fire room compartment

Once fire-fighters arrive at the above situation (Figure No.29) having already secured around the closed up fire room compartment (Steps 1 - 4 inclusive) and 'read the fire gases' inside the fire room compartment (Step 5) confirming the black smoke vacating on the 'over pressure' is 'hot', the use of a "Mitre"[40]

---

[40] The "Mitre" was the name given to a piercing stainless steel tip fitted onto the 'Blaster' style branch/nozzle, because it looked like a bishop's head-dress, following development discussions with myself and Gerry Harris of Blaster Technologies.

style branch/nozzle (A piercing high pressure hose reel branch/nozzle) is the fire-fighter's utopia. If the fire room compartment is closed up and there is 'hot' black smoke inside with no openings to fresh air. We proceed to pierce above the door and inject the application of water spray droplets 0.03 mm, to create total inertia. Then, upon entry there won't even be any fire to fight, because, we have created the desired inertia of the combustible gases (smoke), which is after all what catches fire.

What if the partition above the door to the closed up fire room compartment is breezeblock, brick or stone and the "Mitre" will not be able to pierce it with its car wash style branch/nozzle, even with its stainless steel piercing tip. However, if we have a hand held cordless drill with the right size drill bit already fitted - which is constantly on trickle charge on the Fire Engine/Truck (similar to the hand held lamps) so it is ready to use and it is brought into play and taken on all first strike operations. The drill makes a hole in the solid structure and we then insert the "Mitre". If the masonry proves too formidable for some reason we can then, as a last resort, go through the top of the wooden door to the fire room compartment or, failing all that, revert back to our original standard operational procedures (SOPs) (See Step 5.1). The door should be opened slightly and the water spray droplets injected into the upper part of the fire room compartment before and re-closing the door.

Once the inertia of the closed up fire room compartment has taken place, then, in a synchronised way, not freelance, fire crews positioned outside can break the external window to the closed up fire room compartment. The message is sent to the fire-fighters in charge of the positive pressure ventilation (PPV) fan outside the building/structure adjacent to an external door, to turn on the PPV fan to assist in ventilating all the residual inert black smoke and steam left in the fire room compartment.

Simultaneously the fire attack crew make entry into the fire room compartment having withdrawn the "Mitre" from above the door to the fire room compartment and effect entry to search and rescue and in so doing, bring together all the good practices I've observed. ☺ [41]

It is preferable to use such techniques rather than to risk further the lives

---

[41] In May 1993 I was fortunate enough to arrange a visit for an 18-strong British Fire Service delegation to observe the amalgamation of Swedish fire-fighting techniques and PPV techniques from the USA by my good Spanish friend Miguel Baset, Assistant Chief Fire Officer, Consorci Provincial de Valencia (The Province of Valencia Fire Service). Miguel was a wonderful host and showed us tremendous hospitality and evoked my interest into going one step further and apply inertia techniques to a closed up fire room compartment and practical research into these concepts, began shortly after my return to 'Old Blighty'. I'd like to thank Miguel for his pioneering example and endeavours to improve fire-fighter safety.

of casualties in the fire room/adjacent compartments and their fire-fighting rescuers.

The introduction of such standard operational procedures (SOPs) may be easier for some Fire Services/Departments in North America to implement than for other countries, because of their custom and practice of having Ladder & Rescue Companies. The Rescue Company can make the call to ventilate and the Ladder Company will already be in position.

The use of positive pressure ventilation (PPV) fans is also more prevalent in North America, compared to other parts of the world.

If, Fire Services/Departments in North America, embraced these standard operational procedures (SOPs) and managed to co-ordinate their attack they could leap-frog ahead of Fire and Rescue Services from other countries' and complement their existing professional fire-fighting procedures and become even more integral than they are already and improve to become some of the safest Fire Services/Departments in the world by drastically reducing or better still eradicating in the line of duty deaths (LODD) of fire-fighters, whilst dealing with fire incidents involving flashovers and/or backdrafts.

This would make massive inroads into the annual fire-fighter death tally (LODD) at fire incidents involving flashovers and/or backdrafts, which, as in many other parts of the globe, are unnecessarily high. With an alternative option now available of complementing existing standard operational procedures (SOPs). We can repair the chinks in our armour and remove the blind spots and make the fire-ground an integral, safe and secure place of work for fire-fighters. The truth of the matter is, losing fire-fighters to the devastating effects of flashovers and backdrafts is an unnecessary tragic loss of life and indeed, is preventable.

Why not always apply the "Mitre" inertia techniques as described above?

Apart, from not being applicable for use on cold smoke conditions inside a fire room compartment, unfortunately, not all Fire Services/Departments will have access to the relevant equipment for successful implementation of these alternative techniques, namely, a "Mitre" style piercing branch/nozzle and/or positive pressure ventilation (PPV) fans. Also, some are reluctant to embrace the concept of inertia and the use of positive pressure ventilation (PPV) fans. So, we must provide standard operating procedures (SOPs) that are accessible to all Fire Services/Departments with their current operational equipment.

There is also another scenario where the use of a positive pressure ventilation

(PPV) fans, would not be suitable. What if the closed up fire room compartment did not have an external window (exit port) to facilitate the conventional application of ventilation procedures? E.g. store room or basement room. These are the reasons for working towards providing the relevant realistic fire training in the Fire Development Simulators (FDS). This will enable Fire Services/ Departments to safely and effectively introduce the search and rescue standard operating procedures (SOPs) Steps 1 - 10 (inclusive) described thus far.

If you, do not have positive pressure ventilation (PPV) fans available for operational use, but did have access to a "Mitre" style piercing branch/nozzle, I would recommend you implement the standard operating procedures (SOPs) described up to and including Steps 1 - 5 and then omit using Step 5.1.and introduce the use of Step 5.2. The use of the "Mitre" style piercing branch/nozzle to inert the black 'hot' smoke inside the closed up fire room compartment from outside in the corridor and then proceed to implement Steps 6 – 10 (inclusive) onwards following introduction of Step 5.2.

To assist in evaluating this modus operandi we conducted tests[42] in a Fire Development Simulator (FDS) at the Manchester Airport Fire Service Training Ground. The tests were carried out practically, using thermo-couples inside a closed up fire room compartment (See Figure No. 30 below) to show how the conditions at all levels were improved by a reduction in temperature upon application of the "Mitre" which confirmed application of Step 5.2 cannot make the temperature conditions any worse for casualties inside.

The "Mitre" was introduced at 540 seconds into the test.

During the tests we created several backdrafts in the Fire Development Simulator (FDS). Then, let it smoulder for five minutes before introducing the "Mitre" at 540 seconds. I pierced the plaster/gypsum board partition above the door of the FDS and injected water spray droplets, counting to thirty before I was going to pull the "Mitre" out of the aperture I'd created. By the time I'd counted to twenty eight seconds the 'over pressure' created in the upper part of the closed up fire room compartment had physically pushed the "Mitre" out of the opening under its own steam. All the thermo-couples' (located vertically at top, middle and bottom positions at midway and end points within the FDS) temperature readings nose-dived and the water spray droplets had made the combustible gas layers shrink up into the ceiling and forced the "Mitre" outwards.

---

[42] The tests were facilitated by Steve Ridsdale (Engineer) who kindly volunteered his services for my research free of charge and is also the owner of a fantastic Mexican Restaurant – Fiesta Mehicana, Clifford Street, York, England, which is virtually next door to York Fire Station would you believe! I'd like to take this opportunity to thank Steve for his endeavours in running the tests.

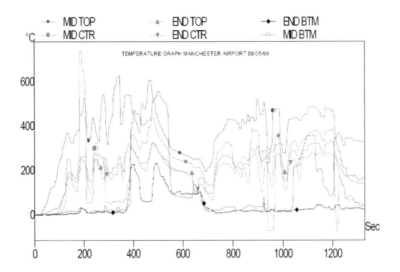

Figure No.30 – Temperature monitoring chart from inside the Fire Development Simulator (FDS)

The creation of 'over pressure' in the ceiling enabled air to enter at the lower parts of the fire room compartment via the 'under pressure' to balance the positive pressure created in the ceiling. The "Mitre" was re-applied at 1200 seconds into the test for 15 seconds this time and then, the fire attack crew entered the closed up fire room compartment following the second withdrawal of the "Mitre". Normally, they would have encountered a possible backdraft scenario, but on this occasion there were no flames to fight and just an inert black smoke layer and steam to be ventilated. Fire-fighting in the future may well become very mundane and boring.

Swedish Training Methods are based upon two basic philosophies:

      1   If you work with FEAR you must TRAIN with FEAR
      2   If you hear something, you will forget it
            If you see something you may remember it
            But if you do something once
            YOU CAN DO IT AGAIN

The fire-fighters' role, when up against the powerful force of nature - fire - can be very harrowing and any fire-fighter who says they have not experienced fear is either not being totally honest or plain dumb. We have to train to overcome the inherent fear that is part of our job; we must acquire knowledge and practice how to deal with ALL the worst-case scenarios we are likely to face on the fire-ground in the real world.

"Nothing in life is to be feared. It is only to be understood". [43]

So, once we have been there, done that (got the tee-shirt) and know what to expect, there are no surprises when it happens for real. You can do it again and go straight into 'offensive mode' without thinking; like a finally tuned machine we spring into action and attack where necessary. If the window fails and a hot 'rich' flashover/backdraft ensues inside the closed up fire room compartment, we do not down tools and run. We go on the attack, because we know we can win. That's why we train to the limits.

Despite the dangerous nature of fire, fire-fighters would be unprepared to meet the real enemy without relevant, responsible and realistic fire development simulated training.

We should count them all out and count them all in. Swedish Health and Safety legislation states, it's a worker's right to expect to come home safely from a day's work and fire-fighters are not exempt from this law in Sweden.

Fire-fighters should be properly prepared to tackle fires, not protected from the reality of fire by training unrealistically, because some sections of the Fire Service/Department feel it is too dangerous to train realistically and claim watching videos, DVD's and studying books is adequate preparation to deal with the dangerous nature of fire development. If we can't control fire during responsible, realistic fire training, what chance do we have when we attend real fires and there are lives at risk and rescues to be performed, whilst simultaneously tackling the fire.

The universal introduction of realistic, responsible and practical fire development training, is now achievable and if supported with solid simple theories, modern fire-fighting equipment and appropriate personal protective equipment, used in conjunction with the correct standard operational procedures (SOPs). Then our fire-fighters can become completely integral, safe and secure on the fire-ground.

Fire has been a great friend to the human race, providing warmth, energy and light for centuries and a powerful adversary during times, when, it gets out of control. However, fighting fires is not like waging wars when your enemy can use newly developed weapons or tactics. Fire development has not changed over the ages and we should after living with it all this time, know and understand it's every move and be able to bring it back under control when it gets out of hand and without the need to sacrifice fire-fighters in the process.

FIRE IS PREDICTABLE AND BEATABLE EVERY TIME!

---

[43] The contents of my fortune cookie acquired during a recent visit to a Chinese Restaurant in Streatham Hill, London

90

PART THREE

COLD SMOKE CONDTIONS

Scenario One – 'Delayed Flashover'

Upon arrival at a house/structure fire, you as part of a fire-fighting crew begin to 'size-up' the fire (Step 1) and confirm that there is a closed up fire room compartment on the ground floor (UK) full of black smoke (rich) and there is a cold grey static smoke layer in the adjacent corridor halfway between the floor and ceiling. Following the ventilation or inertia of this grey smoke layer in the corridor (Steps 2 & 3) and wetting of the wall and ceiling directly above the fire room compartment door (Step 4), you proceed to 'read the fire gases' inside the fire room compartment (Step 5) and are confronted with a 'cold' black smoke layer and the horizontal position of the neutral zone (NZ) is approximately 450mm (18") above floor level, exiting very slowly on 'over pressure' and it does not ignite on contact with air in the adjacent corridor (See Figure No. 31 below).

What do these cold smoke conditions inside the fire room compartment indicate, if we apply The **'Rule of Five'**?

How would you deal with this scenario?

"COLD SMOKE and NO IGNITION OUTSIDE THE FIRE ROOM COMPARTMENT"

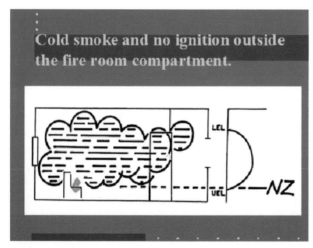

Figure No.31 – Cold smoke and no ignition outside the fire room compartment

One of the most dangerous scenarios a fire-fighter is likely to face is a 'delayed flashover'. When the door to the closed up fire room compartment, is opened the black smoke layer exiting on 'over pressure' comes out lazily and without any real force and seems 'cold' - known as **'cold smoke'.** Why is the smoke cold?

If, upon opening the door the air enters upon the 'air track' via the 'under pressure' and the oxygen deficient layer formed above the surface of the smouldering material (concealed/closed ignition source) is not disturbed and the black smoke layer begins to rise up and away from the ignition source before there is any flame-up, known as **'no flame-up'.** An extremely dangerous scenario for fire-fighters is unfolding and if the door remains open, the 'cold' black smoke layer is progressively moving away from its upper explosive limit (rich) and towards the ideal mixture. Now the fuel (black smoke layer) and concealed/closed ignition source have become detached.

With **'no flame-up',** there is no heat transmitting through the 'air track' via 'over pressure' to the exit port (open door) so the fire-fighters are lulled into a false sense of security. This smoke which, they know, 'burns' should **not** be cooled and made inert, as previously advocated for 'hot' black smoke (conditions) moving with the driving force of a 'backdraft'. If they did, and proceeded into the fire room compartment in the traditional way, leaving the door open to secure their retreat and the 'cold' black smoke layer is progressively getting closer and closer to its ideal mixture, which could contain high-energy combustible gases. In these circumstances a 'delayed flashover' or worse still a 'fire gas explosion' is now becoming a realistic possibility.

The fire-fighters are now crawling into a fire room compartment underneath a **'bomb'** waiting for it to be detonated. If you applied water spray droplets into 'over pressure' region in the above circumstances with the door open and the horizontal position of the neutral zone (NZ) of this high-energy combustible gas (smoke) layer indicating it is close to its ideal mixture, by trying to cool and/or inert the already 'cold' smoke, you could inadvertently disturb the balance of the air flows inside the fire room compartment. This would create turbulence, which could then quite easily disturb the oxygen deficient layer formed above the surface of the smouldering material (concealed/closed ignition source) and produce a flaming brand that could travel upwards towards the high-energy combustible gas (smoke) layer near its ideal mixture on the 'air track'. A 'delayed flashover' could then occur or, worse still, a 'fire gas explosion', and if an explosion did occur under these circumstances it is commonly referred to as a 'cold smoke explosion'.

How can cold smoke explode? Surely it is not hot enough to explode!

Here lies the conundrum.

Temperature alone[44] does not dictate whether or not these high-energy cold combustible gases (smoke) are capable of exploding, but rather their percentage of flammable gases with air. These high-energy combustible gases (smoke) are capable of exploding at approximately 8 bars pressure, if ignited at their ideal mixture. However, an explosion cannot occur until there is an ignition source present, which is provided by the creation of turbulence from the application of water spray droplets into the 'over pressure' region by the fire-fighters, if they choose the traditional methods.

The temperature of the 'cold' smoke may not be hot enough to cause the fire-fighters any perceivable concern, 'cold smoke', doesn't just burn, it can explode. After you have entered the fire room compartment and just as you have let down your guard, because it feels not much warmer than a hot summer's day, the 'cold smoke' inside the fire room compartment can feasibly ignite and explode at approximately 8 bars pressure, which could cause structural damage, let alone fatally injuring the fire-fighters inside.

Fire-fighters must learn to respect all types of combustible gases, especially 'cold smoke' and never become too complacent during fire-fighting operations because one simple mistake can result in irreversible consequences and a lifetime of pain and suffering for their colleagues, friends and families. All because, we did not take the time or trouble to find out all there is to know about this lethal and powerful force of nature, seemingly feeble cold smoke!

---

[44] The Manual of Firemanship: Practical Firemanship III. Part 6C, Her Majesty's Stationary Office (London, 1986) Page 107, states that the flashpoint of petroleum spirit is – 45.6°C (- 50°F), meaning that if an ignition source were introduced into the petrol vapour mixture at below freezing and above - 40°C (fire point), it would still be at a temperature that could facilitate ignition of the petrol vapour.

'Delayed Flashover' - Concealed Ignition Source (C.I.S)

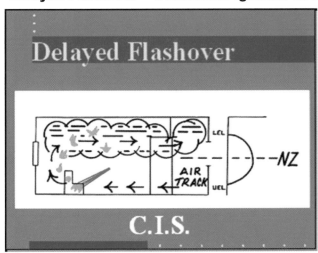

Figure No.32 – 'Delayed Flashover' – Concealed ignition Source (C.I.S)

Even, if fire-fighters do not cool the 'over pressure' region upon entry they are not out of the woods yet, if they leave the door open. Simultaneously as the 'cold' black smoke layer is becoming more and more explosive, visibility for the fire-fighters is becoming much better as the 'cold' black smoke layer rises up and away from the as yet undisturbed, oxygen deficient layer formed above the surface of the smouldering material (concealed/closed ignition source) and travels out of the exit port (open door) on the 'air track' into the adjacent corridor. The fire-fighters eventually locate the smouldering material (concealed/closed ignition source) and in compliance with long established techniques, upon finding the seat of the fire they hit its base with a straight stream branch/nozzle. Sometimes they can also disturb the closed/concealed ignition source during the searching of the fire room compartment for the persons reported missing.

The fire-fighters find the offending smouldering item of furniture and proceed to hit the base of the fire or inadvertently knock into it whilst searching. In doing either of the above, the previously closed/concealed ignition source (smouldering material) is disturbed, releasing a flaming brand (open ignition source), which is picked up by the 'air track' and taken straight into the 'cold' black smoke layer (See Figure No. 32).

This flaming brand provides the open ignition source for the black smoke layer, which is 'cold' but highly flammable and possibly explosive and perhaps in the vicinity of its ideal mixture. The fire attack crew and any casualties inside the fire room compartment could now be engulfed in the ensuing 'delayed flashover/fire gas explosion'.

The 'cold' black smoke layer can expand three to four times its volume, if ignited at its ideal mixture (Fire Gas Explosion - See Photograph No. 4).

The subsequent fireball expands unilaterally, hitting the ceiling and floor simultaneously and takes the least line of resistance, the open doorway, creating an 'over pressure' in the corridor towards the exit port (fresh air). A uniform flame front from floor to ceiling height, exits the fire room compartment. A telltale sign that a 'fire gas explosion' has occurred, is evidence of structural damage on the exit path from the fire room compartment to the exit port via adjacent compartments/corridors en route to the exit port.

The effect on the external window in the fire room compartment, which has already been weakened by pulsations during the smouldering/pulsating stage, could be that it is sucked inwards by the exiting flame front down the corridor. Observers standing outside buildings/structures especially in high-rise buildings/structures, maybe given the false impression that the wind may have blown the window inward, providing the air for the subsequent explosion. A mirage, things are not always what they seem!

A 'fail safe' standard operating procedure (SOP) for dealing with this type of scenario would be to 'shut that door'.[45]

Standard Operating Procedures (SOPs) for 'Delayed Flashover' conditions involving cold smoke.

How do we safely deal with 'delayed flashover' conditions involving 'cold' smoke as depicted in Figure No.31?

After implementing Steps 1 – 4 (inclusive) and upon 'reading the gases' inside the fire room compartment (Step 5), if you as part of a fire-fighting crew are confronted with a black smoke layer exiting on 'over pressure' from approximately 450mm (18") above floor level and the black smoke is 'cold', fire-fighters must proceed by omitting both Steps 5.1 & 5.2 and ensuring that they do not disturb the environment inside the closed up fire room compartment by the introduction of water spray droplets and then proceed to make an entry into the fire room compartment (Step 6) and 'shut that door'. Then, they should also omit the creating of the 'Sauna Effect' (Step 7) and 'Painting the Wall Linings' (Step 8) again to minimise the disturbance of the environment inside the fire room compartment, which is full of 'cold' black

---

[45] Larry Grayson was a popular British comedian and his catch phrase was 'shut that door'.

smoke and because the Security Officer has closed the door too onto the hose reel/hose and with the black smoke being 'cold' the beneficial effects of inertia will be minimal. Additionally, because the environment is 'cold', the wall linings will not be that warm and the likelihood of the external window failing is negligible due to the lack of pulsations and therefore not as imperative for fire-fighters to have acquired the 'heat tolerance' limits required when dealing with 'hot' black smoke inside a closed up fire room compartment.

Also, remember following the satisfactory completion of the search and rescue procedures inside the fire room compartment they can carefully and gently begin dampening down of the original closed/concealed ignition source (Step 9), fire-fighting crew should proceed to withdraw from the fire room compartment and omit ventilating from inside (Step 10) and close the door to the now, person free fire room compartment and ventilate externally, by either breaking or opening the external window and allow the room to naturally ventilate, having removed all personnel and resources from the path of any subsequent 'cold smoke delayed flashover', which includes inside the building/structure. Then, following completion of the natural ventilation of the fire room compartment, fire-fighters can return inside to complete turning over/overhaul procedures.

If the configuration of the fire room compartment will not facilitate external ventilation, because it does not have any windows opening to fresh air e.g. storerooms, basements etc. then the 'cold smoke' will have to be allowed to naturally ventilate to the fresh air via the nearest external opening, but before this procedure is implemented personnel and resources should be removed from the path of the any subsequent 'cold smoke delayed flashover', which involves temporary withdrawal from the building/structure by all fire service personnel and careful consideration should be given to how the door to the fire room compartment can be opened remotely to facilitate a safe exit by fire-fighters, before the natural ventilation begins to become effective e.g. by pulling a line tied around the handle of the slightly open fire room compartment door.

The recommended standard operating procedures (SOPs) for dealing with these particular 'cold' smoke' conditions, outlined above, may at first glance seem a little extreme and over cautious, but believe me some of the case histories,[46] I've researched prove that they are not.

If you recognise that this 'cold smoke' layer is an unexploded 'bomb' laying in wait to be detonated, these standard operating procedures (SOPs) do not seem at all extreme. Bomb disposal officers would treat the scene of an

---

[46] Case Histories are described in my forthcoming book, "SIZE UP" – Fire-fighting Tactics and on our website **www.smokeburns.com**

unexploded bomb with great care and not allow any unnecessary disturbance of the scene and if you, as a fire-fighter truly comprehend 'smoke burns' and can explode, especially 'cold smoke' containing 'high-energy' combustible gases, then these standard operating procedures (SOPs) should not be a quantum 'leap of faith'. Indeed, if you consider the consequences of being complacent and ignoring the realistic, although remote, possibility of creating a 'cold smoke delayed flashover', which can cause fatalities from the subsequent devastating effects of the 'delayed flashover'. Then, I personally would not be prepared to take such a risk and believe that any Incident Commander in charge of this type of incident, has a legal and moral 'duty of care' for fire-fighters and members of the public alike and if you ignore these extremely dangerous 'cold smoke' conditions and a 'cold smoke delayed flashover' does occur under your command, it will from now on, be extremely difficult to plead ignorance and state that 'fire is unpredictable' as mitigating circumstances for your actions.

I also feel very uncomfortable in using some of the current aspects of the **'Tactical Ventilation'** techniques[47], which recommend for black smoke conditions inside a closed up fire room compartments (possibly containing cold black smoke), breaking the external window of the fire room compartment from outside and then effecting entry leaving the door in the open position. If you do not control the fire (previously contained prior to ventilation), it can ignite or explode and the subsequent flame fronts could seriously injure any fire-fighters and casualties inside the fire room compartment at the time of ignition. Simultaneously, the subsequent free flaming fire could get away from you inside the building/structure by developing inwardly and upwards away from the fire room compartment and create uncontrolled fire spread, as well as flaming off through the broken window.

Additionally, if there is 'cold' black smoke inside the closed up fire room compartment and 'Tactical Ventilation' techniques are deployed by breaking an external window and fire-fighters, then choose to blow the 'cold smoke' out of the newly created exit port (window) with a positive pressure ventilation (PPV) fan[48]. The air forced into the fire room compartment from the positive pressure ventilation (PPV) fan could have exactly the same effect as that of the application of a straight stream branch/nozzle as described in the 'cold smoke delayed flashover' scenario (See Figure No. 32) by disturbing

---

[47] Fire Service Manual: Compartment Fires and Tactical Ventilation.
Volume 2, Fire Service Operations, HM Fire Service Inspectorate Publications Section, London: The Stationary Office (1997) Page 10
[48] Fire Service Manual: Compartment Fires and Tactical Ventilation.
Volume 2, Fire Service Operations, HM Fire Service Inspectorate Publications Section, London: The Stationary Office (1997) Pages 51 & 55

the oxygen deficient layer formed above the surface of the smouldering material (concealed/closed ignition source). If you study Figure No.32 and in your minds eye replace the straight stream water jet with forced air from a positive pressure ventilation (PPV) fan, the positive flowing air could quite easily disturb the previously closed/concealed ignition source (smouldering material) releasing a flaming brand, which is picked up by the 'air track' and taken straight into the detached 'cold' black smoke layer that could be in the vicinity of its ideal mixture.

The deployment these PPV techniques and procedures in the above circumstances could in my view result in the Fire Service/Department inadvertently blowing up the building/structure.

Scenario Two - 'Cold Smoke Explosion' (Mobile Gas Cloud)

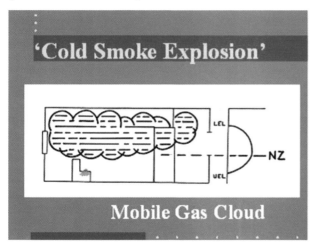

Figure No 33 - 'Cold Smoke Explosion'

What, if, as a member of an operational fire-fighting crew, you have secured around a closed up fire compartment by implementing Steps 1 – 4 (inclusive) and then you 'read the fire gases' inside the closed up fire room compartment (Step 5), expecting to observe the black smoke inside the fire room compartment being down to approximately 450 mm (18") above floor level (rich) and to your amazement the 'cold' black smoke layer confronting you, is already at the halfway horizontal position approximately equidistant from the floor and ceiling level and is 'cold' (See Figure No. 33 above), and it seems to be static with very little movement. What is the horizontal position of the neutral zone (NZ) of this 'cold' black smoke layer indicating to you?

98

How would you deal with such a scenario?

Have you ever in your operational service encountered similar circumstances?

What are the inherent dangers with this scenario?

Can you apply, The **'Rule of Five' (MITCH)** to diagnosis what stage of this particular fire is at?

I'd never even considered it previously as a possibility and when it came to my attention that such circumstances had occurred and I was asked, what would I have done?

My response was to say I'd quickly close the door again, not because of any insight or wisdom, but to buy myself some thinking time to evaluate where the real danger lies, having never before been confronted with such a scenario.

The danger is clear and present. I am being confronted by a highly explosive and combustible mobile gas cloud inside a building/structure that has already become detached from its original closed/concealed ignition source. Therefore am unable to maintain a rich mixture as advocated thus far, because the 'cold' smoke (combustible gas) layer is already in the vicinity at its ideal mixture and could be explosive. I cannot put the lives of the fire-fighters at risk by committing them underneath a 'bomb' or endanger others inside and outside of the building/structure by disturbing this 'cold' smoke layer and possibly creating an explosion.

In these circumstances if there are any persons to be rescued inside the fire room compartment in my view it is reasonable to assume, if they are on the floor then air will be available to them or if they're conscious, escape under their own steam is a distinct possibility. Hence there is no immediate necessity to perform a rescue by deploying fire-fighters underneath a 'bomb'.

What are my options?

With there being no imperative rescue to perform or any free burning fire to fight. I do not want to commit fire-fighters into the fire room compartment room and possibly disturb the closed/concealed ignition source and instigate an explosion.

What I need to do is allow the 'cold' smoke explosive mobile gas cloud to disperse by allowing it to naturally ventilate out of the external window, ensuring that the door to the fire room compartment remains closed to minimise the turbulence. Then, I'd withdraw my fire-fighting personnel and resources from the path of any possible 'cold smoke explosion' before ventilating the fire room compartment by gently breaking the external window. Then, when the inherent danger of this mobile gas cloud has evaporated into the atmosphere, it will be safe to commit fire-fighting crews inside the fire room compartment to search for any casualties and dampen down the original closed/concealed ignition source and commence turning over/overhaul procedures in a safe working environment.

The real incident that this particular fire relates to is one of the case histories to be evaluated and discussed in my forthcoming book:

"SIZE UP" – Fire-fighting Tactics.

CHAPTER EIGHT

The ROLLOVER

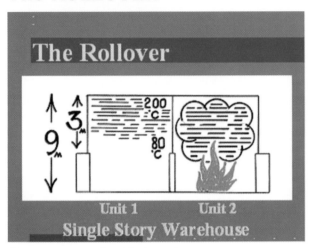

Figure No.34 – The 'Rollover'

The sixth type of flashover is called **The 'Rollover'.**

The above scenario shows a fire in the right hand side of the single storey warehouse, with the external door to this compartment open. Unit 1 on the left hand side has light grey smoke in the ceiling, approximately six metres above floor level. There is a fire-resisting party wall between both sides of the warehouse.

If you were asked, whilst, performing the role of a crew commander, to deploy a fire-fighting crew into Unit 1 from the left hand side of the above warehouse, to assess the possible fire spread potential, would you have any reservations about putting your fire service personnel under a three metre deep grey smoke layer in a single storey warehouse, with no apparent involvement from the fire in the adjacent premises, other than this light grey smoke layer?

If, there are any dangers to consider, what are they?

And, as the great bard 'William Shakespeare' once said....
"This above all: to thine own self be true". – Hamlet (Act I, Scene III).[49]

Be honest, would you deploy a fire-fighting crew?

---

[49] http://absoluteshakespeare.com/trivia/quotes/quotes.htm

Before I had been to Sweden, I would have had no problem in committing a fire-fighting crew to perform the above task and would not have had any idea of the inherent dangers involved in their deployment. Do we really understand 'smoke burns'?

How many traditionalists would commit a fire-fighting crew underneath a grey smoke layer?

If your two fire-fighters were committed into Unit 1 to check if there had been any fire spread from Unit 2 into Unit 1 and they travelled under the grey smoke layer with a water spray branch/nozzle and reached the closed connecting door 100 metres into the building/structure. Then opened the connecting door to assess the fire contained in Unit 2 and dispatched a message of the fire conditions via their radio communications to the Incident Commander and began to retrace their steps, having closed the connecting door.

There is a distinct possibility that approximately three to four minutes later, under the right conditions, that a fireball could shoot out of the external entrance door to Unit 1, some thirty metres across the street and the two fire-fighters would be totally engulfed in this fireball and could be seriously injured or killed. Fire-fighters outside might be reluctant to go inside to rescue their colleagues, because they may have never experienced anything like this and are too frightened to help their colleagues.

WHAT HAS HAPPENED?

The accumulation of the grey smoke in Unit 1 was caused by seepage from the fire in Unit 2. The black smoke had seeped through gaps in the walls and joints of the fire barrier that may consist of panels insulated with mineral wool, that have satisfied fire resistance testing criteria and been accepted by both Building Control and Fire Safety Departments. However, there are a couple of problems with using materials like this. Firstly, even the manufacturers' literature states the material is fire resisting and will prevent flame penetration and remain integral, but it does not have any 'hot' smoke resistance properties, because at the time of writing there was no current 'hot' smoke resistance test, only a smoke resistance test at ambient temperatures.[50]

So if, smoke, which we have already shown can burn, is capable of travelling through fire-resisting panels insulated with mineral wool. We are allowing combustible gases to collect the other side of a fire-resisting barrier.

---

[50] British Standards BS 476: Part 31:1983. Method of measuring smoke penetration through door sets and shutter assemblies Section 31.1 Method of measurement under ambient temperature conditions.

All it needs now to spread the fire is an ignition source.

In my view we should create a valid effective 'hot' smoke resistance test for materials and incorporate this into the standards for fire resistance, if it is to realistically prevent the spread of fire. The other problem with fire-resisting panels insulated with mineral wool is that, unless exceptional workmanship is exercised, there is a tendency for it to have gaps especially after services (cables and piping) have been installed. These gaps have breached the fire resistance of the fire-resisting panels insulated with mineral wool, also leaving gaps for the smoke to get through. Nowadays, this is more prevalent in the age of computer communications and vast amounts of cables transporting information throughout buildings/structures. The integrity of flexible materials, such as, fire-resisting panels insulated with mineral wool may come into question because of the standard of workmanship.

In Figure No.34 the black smoke from Unit 2 has seeped into Unit 1 and has now turned grey due to mixing with the oxygen. It has begun to accumulate in the ceiling progressively increasing in volume in the ceiling of Unit 1, getting closer and closer to its lower explosive limit as time goes on. The analogy of 200°C in the ceiling and 80°C at the horizontal position of the neutral zone (NZ) is to emphasise the temperature is warmest in the ceiling and as previously explained, when combustible gases (smoke) are heated up, then the energy absorption of the air becomes less effective and the grey smoke is getting progressively closer to its lower explosive limit on the flammable range. Therefore the probability of the grey smoke at ceiling level being at its lower explosive limit is greater, than the grey smoke at the horizontal position of the neutral zone (NZ) on the bottom edge of the grey smoke layer. Therefore, the grey smoke is more likely to ignite at upper ceiling level first, being nearer its lower explosive limit.

Figure No. 35 – The 'Rollover' (Progressive Lean Flashover)
Ignites and begins to roll

As the fire-fighters open the connecting door to assess the fire in Unit 2 a 'hot' black smoke layer could exit from the fire in Unit 2 on 'over pressure' and travel on the 'air track' into Unit 1 and ascend into the ceiling.

If within this 'hot' black smoke layer there is a flaming brand, then fire-fighters have unwittingly allowed an 'open ignition source' to go into the grey smoke layer and if the combustible gases at ceiling level are at or past their lower explosive limit they could be ignited by the flaming brand. By this time the fire-fighters have closed the connecting door and have begun to retrace their steps. This is the beginning of a progressive 'lean flashover' in the ceiling.

The grey smoke in the ceiling is at its lower explosive limit and the flaming brand/open ignition source has ignited the combustible gases (smoke), which now produce a free burning flame. This transmits heat to the adjacent grey smoke rapidly making it flammable and before we know it, we have a rapid **'progressive lean flashover'** traversing unilaterally across a ceiling with a massive cubic area at approximately 660°C, coincidentally the approximate thermal ignition temperature of carbon monoxide (CO).

The vast majority of materials used in the modern day construction of these single storey warehouses, when heated, begin to de-compose and give off large amounts of high-energy combustible gases (black smoke) due to their high calorific value. As a result the 'Rollover' in the ceiling now produces large amounts of downward and sideways radiation below and around the flame front, which decomposes these materials, producing massive amounts of black smoke. As the flame front continues laterally it quickly reaches all four walls of the building/structure, but as it is still expanding which way will it travel now?

It will travel downwards towards the air supply (the open external door) on 'over pressure' via the 'air track'.

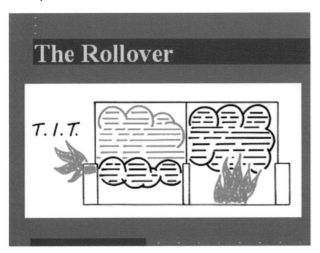

Figure No.36 – The 'Rollover' exits the building into the street

The 'Rollover' really begins to pick up momentum and if there were any fire-fighters caught below this 'Rollover', even if they were Olympic sprinters, they'd struggle to run fast enough to escape the ensuing fireball. The downward radiation now intensifies and creates a larger black smoke layer below the flame front, which is too rich to burn. However, due to the high temperatures being transmitted through the black smoke layer, the combustible gases soon reach their thermal ignition temperature. So, as the flame front forces the black smoke layer below it down towards the open door to the street from Unit 1, it creates a certain amount of turbulence. The bottom of the black smoke layer (horizontal position of the neutral zone) starts picking up air, which mixes with the black smoke at its thermal ignition temperature.

If, you are unfortunate enough to be below this massive force of nature, you will see pockets of blue flame (rich) spontaneously igniting along the lowest layer of the black smoke.

NOW is time to pick your window!!

So, if the black smoke layer is igniting at its thermal ignition temperature inside the building, what effect will the mass exodus of this black smoke layer full of high-energy gases at their thermal ignition temperature have on events as it hits the air in the street? It will ignite on contact with air and create a massive fireball across the street sucking out most of the remaining black smoke and burning combustible gases (flames) from inside the building out into the street. It is now what one might call spent, with the majority of the fuel out in the open air. What you are left with is a seriously injured or fatally wounded fire-fighters at floor level and any combustible materials at floor level flaming off, but not a realistic likelihood of a repeat performance due to lack of fuel over a large cubic area.

Now, it is relatively safe to commit crews to rescue the marooned fire-fighters, whilst being vigilant regarding any possible collapse of the weakened structure. However, if you have never been here before or trained to understand fire development would you go back in, certain that there would not be another 'Rollover'?

After realising the 'mechanism of fire' and the sequence of events leading up to a 'Rollover', would you put fire-fighters underneath a grey smoke layer in the ceiling of a single storey warehouse six metres above their heads with possibly 100 metres to retrace their steps back to the entry point and only 450 litres per minute of water to fight a possible flame front covering 10,000 square metres. As an Incident Commander, you would surely not commit your fire-fighters into these conditions, knowing what I've described above to be a distinct possibility.

If, however, you ignored this possibility and unfortunately a 'Rollover' occurs you as Incident Commander are now responsible for the deaths of any future fire-fighters sent unnecessarily underneath a flammable gas cloud without the wherewithal to deal with the ensuing 'Rollover'.

"A mistake is not an error until you refuse to correct it". ☺ [51]

We did not know any better in the past, but we do now and can no longer cling to that comfort blanket –'Fire is unpredictable'.

A 'Rollover' is most definitely predictable.

---

[51] A quote on a poster hanging on the office wall of the then, Manchester City Football Club Manager, Stuart Pearce (Psycho) - English Football (Soccer) legend.(The Guardian Weekend Magazine – Saturday 5 May 2007).

REMEDIAL ACTIONS

We cannot commit fire-fighters underneath these flammable gas clouds any longer.

Standard Operating Procedures (SOPs)

Let us re-visit conditions upon arrival of the Fire Service/Department in Figure No.34 - The 'Rollover'. We must firstly secure around the fire and remove the fuel (grey smoke). This will involve developing techniques in using aerial appliances with water spray protection and breathing apparatus for aerial appliance cage operators.

Their first port of call will be to ventilate Unit 1 on one corner at roof level furthest away from Unit 2 and allow the grey smoke layer to disperse, removing the fuel in the building before committing fire-fighters into Unit 1.

If natural ventilation is struggling after creating the roof opening and the ignition source in Unit 2 is still isolated from the fuel (grey smoke) in Unit 1 then you can consider helping the ventilation procedure by using branch/nozzles to perform water fogging ventilation techniques and direct water spray droplets horizontally across the opening, creating 'over pressure' (positive) which will increase the speed of extraction of the grey smoke on leaving the exit port and effectively suck the smoke out of Unit 1, while also providing a protective water spray curtain for fire-fighters in the cage of the aerial appliance if the 'Rollover' ignites.

We cannot justify endangering fire-fighters by deploying them under a grey smoke layer in single storey warehouses/shops any more. It's too dangerous.

At this point I'd also like to lay to rest a myth about these types of combustible gas layers, originating in Sweden and which has been unfortunately adopted as a 'fail safe' elsewhere in the world.

In these circumstances it was explained to me that if upon entry into Unit 1 and fire-fighters fired water spray droplets from their branch/nozzle into the grey smoke layer directly above their heads and droplets came back down and hit them, it was safe to enter into the building beneath the grey smoke layer. Since the water droplets have come back down, the temperature of the grey smoke layer must be below 100°C, otherwise the droplets would have turned to steam and not come back down as water and you could suspect flames are running the ceiling.

This is in my view could be a **fatal** miscalculation because some high-energy gases can ignite at their lower explosive limit at temperatures below 100°C, which makes them capable of being ignited by a flaming brand regardless, in my opinion this is not good practice.

GOOD PRACTICE:

Ventilate the grey smoke layer every time before deploying fire attack crews.

Don't deploy fire-fighting crews underneath a grey smoke layer in a single storey warehouse because 'smoke burns'.

Predict and protect by removing the risk.

Don't deploy fire-fighting crews into any fire/smoke situation without the availability of a water spray branch/nozzle.

'Managing the Risk' is enshrined in the concept of 'Risk Management'.[52]

It should be mandatory to deal with the smoke, to prevent rapid-fire spread and stop the predictable 'rollover'.

Why have we still got fire-fighters running out of buildings/structures on fire being chased by a 'Rollover' with unfortunately not all of them making it...why are we still surprised it is still happening?

[52] **'The Management of Health and Safety at Work Regulations 1999'**, ISBN 0 11 085625 2, Management Regulations 1992 Health and Safety (UK)
http://www.opsi.gov.uk/SI/si1999/19993242.htm

CONCLUSIONS

Other Applications

The concept of 'smoke burns' has been well established and if you accept this Principle then it makes sense to recognise the problems fire-fighters are likely to contend with when they are faced with black smoke in a closed up fire room compartment and grey smoke in the adjacent compartments due to seepage from the fire room compartment. The first consideration in these instances is to secure around the fire, by removal or inertia of the grey smoke before even preparing to tackle the fire room compartment.

Fire-fighters can apply these basic principles to other types of fire compartments containing black smoke and neighbouring compartments with grey smoke, Such as:

1. Suspended ceiling in offices, shops and hotel buildings.
2. Multiple suspended ceilings in retail and educational single storey building.
3. Roof Voids.
4. Basements and
5. High-Rise buildings.

The common theme in these fires is that once you reach the closed up fire room compartment containing the black smoke and grey smoke outside, above or below the fire room compartment, you can begin to 'read the fire gases' and in Fire Service/Department terms, begin your 'Size Up' (of the situation) which will tell you that the fire room compartment does not have a free flow of air on the 'air track' to the seat of the fire and as long as the fire-fighters manage this 'air track' (air management), then the fire can not break out of the fire compartment. Why are the fire-fighters attending this fire? Is it to fight the fire or perform the rescue of any persons trapped by the fire? The fire is the catalyst for the presence of the fire-fighters; their primary role is to perform rescues. If the fire can be safely kept at bay or put away while these rescues are performed, that would be my chosen path every time.

The only discernable difference is the size of the compartment, that the black smoke is contained in, be that laterally, vertically or both. The standard operating procedures (SOPs) should be the same in principle.

Secure around the closed up fire room compartment by removing or cooling the grey smoke in all the adjoining compartments and then, dependent upon the conditions after you've 'read the fire gases' inside the closed up fire room compartment (Step 5) choose the correct method according to the diagnosis of the fire conditions and apply the next designated step by containing or dealing with the black smoke accordingly and safely complete the search and rescue operations.

These basic principles and standard operating procedures (SOPs) have been discussed at length for a single closed up fire room compartment and to apply them further to other types of buildings/structures outlined above (Page 109) is more complicated and is the subject of my forthcoming book:

"SIZE UP" – Fire-fighting Tactics

Case histories of fires from various parts of the world, some of which there have been sadly, fire-fighter fatalities (LODD) will be used for educational purposes. The scene will be set upon the arrival of the Fire Service/Department and the reader will be asked:

How would you deploy your fire attack crews?

Then, followed by a description of what actually occurred at the real incident.

And, finally, I shall offer an alternative deployment based on the theory of 'smoke burns' and the reader can judge for themselves the merits of each approach and make an informed choice of whether there is enough evidence to justify a change in direction and an introduction of the **NEW ORDER** of things.

SIZE UP & AIR MANAGEMENT

SIZE UP

Fire-fighters should be able to 'read the fire gases' and identify the 'air flows' upon arrival at the incident. They must establish what stage the fire is at and confirm by evaluating where it is getting its air, what it is doing and more importantly, if left unchecked, which way it could go.

AIR MANAGEMENT

Then, the fire-fighter can make a diagnosis of the status quo and make an informed decision, based on thorough knowledge and understanding of the 'mechanism of fire' from A to Z, because they fully comprehend 'smoke burns'.

Fire-fighters use their intelligence to beat the fire by having a greater awareness of the route it may choose. They can also direct the path of the fire by taking control of the airflow; then the fire-fighters can prepare to tackle the fire at its predictable destination. In my opinion, fire is predictable and we can beat it every time, if we provide the correct knowledge, equipment and training to bring about the 'New Order' of things.

However, the standard operating procedures (SOPs) discussed in this book cannot be implemented safely or responsibly without the provision of appropriate water spray fire-fighting branches/nozzles,[53] personal protective equipment (PPE),[54] realistic, safe practical training, and the use of Fire Development Simulators (FDS), similar to the one that I designed and developed for use by Manchester Airport Fire Service (UK) to enable us to train their fire-fighting personnel in all the aspects of the standard operating procedures (SOPs) covered thus far in this book. To demonstrate this can be achieved safely, we have been using the Fire Development Simulator (FDS) since 1997 and have never had one single burn injury to the fire-fighters participating in the training. This is a reflection of the professionalism, tremendous ability, enthusiasm and sheer hard work of the compartment fire behaviour training (CFBT) Instructors at Manchester Airport Fire Service.

I'd also like to take this opportunity to thank both, Chief Fire Officer - Chris Formby and Senior Airport Fire Officer - Mark Lakin for their continual support in facilitating CFBT and Research into Fire Development at the Manchester Airport Fire Service Training Ground for which am truly grateful.

---

[53] For example - The 'Mitre' and 'Fogfighter' style water spray branches/nozzles.

[54] In addition, to normal turnout fire gear and breathing apparatus with radio communications provision of flash hoods, over hoods, natural fibre under garments, "Huhta" style water proof fire-fighting gloves, fire tunics with thumb loops (turnout gear) and leather fire boots are required.

Failure to provide the required knowledge, equipment and training would leave me feeling like the author of this excellent poem, written by a Sapper in the Royal Engineers of the Eighth Army whilst in an Egyptian Desert. Having volunteered to fight Hitler and been away from home fighting for two years and, by late 1941, with no sign of an improvement in their fighting capability, he penned this poem:

'MEN ENGLAND FORGOT' (MEF)

Here is the story of men in their glory
  Who fought in desert all bloody and gory.
Who think of Old England, who think of them not.
  Who go by the title 'Men England Forgot'

They live in sand holes quite used to it now
  They dream of old blighty
The Sickle and Plough
  They're "browned off" with shellfire, shrapnel and shot.

They're out in the desert with sandstorms all day.
  They left behind them their good jobs and good pay,
But why should they worry? Who cares who gets shot?
  What's the odds anyway, they're only
    MEN ENGLAND FORGOT.

They're told at the office the same sorry tale
  When they ask for their papers, their parcels or mail,
But they're unlucky. It's part of the plot
  They're only the Army England FORGOT.

The days turn into months, the months into years,
  They live with their worries, heartaches and fears,
God bless you and keep you
    MEN ENGLAND FORGOT.

Sapper William (Bill) Taylor. 8th Army - November 1941 (A desert in Egypt)

The Eighth Army and my father's fortunes changed dramatically for the better within nine months, upon the arrival of Lieutenant-General (later Field Marshall) Bernard Law Montgomery (Monty) and the introduction of a 'New Order'.

The introduction of realistic training and the arrival of much needed equipment and supplies, provided by the United States of America, was accompanied by an appreciation that you have get to know your enemy (Field Marshall Erwin Rommel), before you can win. Lieutenant-General Montgomery recognised the need to provide the realistic knowledge, equipment and training to enable the Eighth Army to complete the tasks asked of them, resulting in the landmark victory at El Alamein in November 1942 and my father taking the first of many steps back to Old Blighty, thankfully.

The moral of this story being, how to be creative and get your beloved father's Wartime poem published, but really it is to learn from Lieutenant-General Montgomery's fine example of leadership qualities. In my opinion Fire Services/Departments should acknowledge the training required to implement these recommended standard operating procedures (SOPs) to protect our fire-fighters from their enemy - FIRE.

We owe a debt of gratitude to the fallen fire-fighters of the world and their families. If, we are to learn from the past and their ultimate sacrifice. We are morally bound to provide all fire-fighters with the best knowledge, equipment and training available.

The greatest tribute and testimony we could bestow in recognition of the sacrifice of our fallen fire-fighters would be the introduction of the 'New Order' and never again allow fire-fighters to be seriously injured or killed, whilst performing their noble task of fighting our common foe – **fire.**

The knowledge, equipment and training needed to introduce this 'New Order' are now readily available to bring this vision to fruition.

EPILOGUE

The theory of 'smoke burns' and the standard operating procedures (SOPs) I've advocated in this book are based on theories developed in Sweden as long ago as 1976. It took another twelve years for word to spread throughout Sweden, with the message falling upon the deaf ears of the persons in the corridors of power, who could have brought about the necessary changes to prevent fire-fighter fatalities in Sweden, which were averaging at the time three fire-fighters a year,[55] in the line of duty deaths (LODD) whilst fire-fighting.

The tragic deaths of two Swedish fire-fighters at a fire incident, involving a flashover, in 1986, prompted the fire-fighters through their representative body (Union) to demand the introduction of a 'New Order'.

The culmination of these events was perfect timing for Anders Lauren (Brandmaster/Station Officer with Stockholm Brandforsvar/Fire and Rescue Service) to provide his gift to the fire-fighters of the world and introduced the concept of using converted steel freight containers as Fire Development Simulators (FDS), providing a simulator to begin to understand the theories and practise with the equipment the new techniques required to prevent fire-fighters from being seriously injured or killed by a flashover or backdraft. These containers are in universal use for haulage, all over the world and therefore this concept could be easily replicated elsewhere at relatively low costs, compared to the provision of conventionally built fire training buildings/structures.

The virtual over night introduction of this 'New Order' by the Swedish Fire and Rescue Services,[56] including both theoretical and realistic practical training in 1986, has drastically reduced fire-fighter fatalities at fires in Sweden. In fact since 1986, there has only been one fire-fighter in the line of duty death (LODD), attributed to fire development conditions worsening, which was in 2003. There was also two other fire-fighter in the line of duty deaths (LODD) in the early 1990's, occurring during suppression after the extinguishing phase.[57] These tragic in the line of duty deaths (LODD) of three Swedish fire-fighters during the last twenty one years was not because of a lack of commitment to providing a safer working environment for fire-fighters.

The reality is that sixty Swedish families are not enduring the pain and

---

[55] Malmsten, C & Rosander, M. "Smoke diving and other tasks with breathing apparatus" The National Board of Occupational Safety and Health, (Sweden, 1987) Giro-brand ab. Page 11
[56] Smoke Diving Guidelines, AFS 1986:6, (Sweden) came into force on 1 January 1987
[57] E-mail dated 29 January 2007 from Colin McIntyre, Statistician, Swedish Rescue Services Agency.

suffering of losing their loved one in a fire because they brought about the changes needed to introduce the 'New Order' and if that is not a bigger enough precedent and a tremendous advert to justify change. I don't know what is! "El futuro va a resultar mejor" ("The future will be better").

The British Fire Service, sadly, had to wait for a similar experience before the changes needed began to be introduced. In February 1996, two fire-fighters died in a house/structure fire in Blaina. South Wales. Then, less than a week later another fire-fighter died in a shopping store fire in Bristol, Avon.

Both fire incidents involved rapid-fire development, which contributed to these fire-fighter fatalities and the realisation for the need to change was recognised and supported by an improvement notice being served on the South Wales Fire Authority by the Health and Safety Executive HSE.[58]

The introduction of realistic compartment fire behaviour training (CFBT) in the UK was to be one of the fastest changes ever witnessed by the British Fire Service and although not mandatory, guidance was available and the majority of brigades introduced some form of practical CFBT and the UK replicated the benefits already seen in Sweden and The British Fire Service did not sustain any fire-fighter fatalities (LODD), because of the effects of a flashover or backdraft during fire-fighting operations from 1996 until 2004. When, sadly two fire-fighters died in the line of duty in Bethnal Green, London. Followed four months later, by a further two fire-fighter fatalities in a High-Rise block of flats in Stevenage, Hertfordshire, whilst fire-fighting, both these incidents involved rapid-fire development as the main culprit responsible for the fatalities.

Up until 1996 UK fire-fighter fatalities figures were similar those in Sweden before 1986. We were losing on average two fire-fighters a year in fires involving flashovers and/or backdrafts. We eradicated these deaths for eight years and reduced them to zero and then, suddenly in 2004 they reverted back to pre-1996 fire-fighter fatality (LODD) figures.

Where is our blind spot? I believe that we have taken our foot of the gas, so to speak. The British Fire Service has been very proactive in introducing CFBT and this contributed to the tremendous reduction in fire-fighter fatalities in the UK from 1996 - 2004.

In my opinion, the provision of responsible, realistic and practical CFBT should become mandatory for all UK Fire Services and not just advisory with supportive guidance. Some of the misinterpretations of CFBT that have been discussed earlier in this book and some of the misconceptions of the Swedish

---

[58] The Health and Safety Executive (UK) served an improvement notice with covering letter to South Wales Fire Authority on 29 July 1996 Ref: JHET/1/LET104.

theories, being practised and used upon the fire-ground, may if not corrected also contribute to maintaining the status quo regarding current fire-fighter injuries and fatalities resulting from the devastating effects of flashovers and backdrafts in the UK.

If fire-fighters are taught to 'read the fire gases' and develop their 'size-up' skills, they will begin to understand the dynamics and relevance of 'under pressure', 'over pressure' and the 'neutral zone' and how to take control of the 'air flows' and make these 'air tracks' work for you, then they can learn to control the fire.

The 'rule of five' will keep you alive.

I've tried my best to identify in this book my own personal views on where I feel fire-fighting operations have chinks in their armour and blind spots, but am not in a position of authority to sanction what I feel are much needed changes to improve the safety of fire-fighters on the fire-ground.

But, if you're able to influence change, I'd ask you to seriously consider introducing the 'New Order' as described in this book and reflect on the fire-fighters role, constantly performing rescues under extremely dangerous and arduous conditions and to fully comprehend the scope of their dedication to duty.

Please peruse the following extract from the Prologue of Gordon Honeycombe's amazing book 'Red Watch'[59] which is part of a marvellous speech given to the Brixton Rotary Club on Tuesday 30 October 1973 by the then Chief Fire Officer of London Fire Brigade – Joe Milner:

> *'A few months before this, another fire raged in the basement of a restaurant. Two firemen in breathing apparatus made their way into the ground floor of the building. Moments later those outside heard a great roar – saw a flash of flame engulf the ground floor and belch out into the street both men were burned – severely burned. Taken to hospital, they were suspended above their beds, for there was no unburned part of their bodies on which they could lie. For three days they suffered; and then, one shortly after the other died. They paid the full price and, some might say much more…..'*

Fire-fighting is one of the best jobs in the world, done by some of the best people that I've ever met in my life and who are prepared to risk their own life to rescue people they don't even know.

Fire-fighters give of their all and they deserve the best.

---

[59] Honeycombe, G, "Red Watch", Hutchinson & Co (Publishers) Ltd. 1976 Page 21/

Acknowledgements

I would not have been able to formulate this book without the friendship, wise counsel and knowledge of some wonderful people, unfortunately there are far too many to mention everybody, but you all know who you are and I'd like to sincerely thank you one and all for your support and wisdom over the years, for which, I am truly grateful.

I'd also like to say a special thank you to Mavis Garratt, my brother-in-law's (Nick) mother a retired English teacher, who has been wonderful in editing this book and shown amazing patience with me and my quirks and my eldest son Joseph William Taylor (Frank) currently working for the Voluntary Service Overseas organisation in London, following a 12 month placement in Malawi last year for his incredible patience with my IT skills or lack of them and for teaching me how to use footnotes.

My two other sons – Trooper Neil Samuel Taylor (Ramage) of Her Majesty's Royal Dragoon Guards and Thomas Peter Taylor (low maintenance) currently saving for a year out in Australia, have both been tremendous sources of inspiration and encouragement and seemed to know instinctively, when I needed support and it was with a great sense of pride that I observed Neil and Thomas participate in their first burn in a Fire Development Simulator (FDS) under the watchful eyes of Gary West, Graham Ware and Ian Roberts.

The stalwart of the team has always been Ian Roberts (Jack) who has tirelessly assisted me following our chance meeting (serendipity) in September 1995. I cannot express in words adequately my gratitude for his constant support, good humour and most of all friendship, without which this book would not have been completed.

Last, but definitely not least is Linda Elizabeth Rice, my long suffering and beautiful wife, who has supported and encouraged me and taken great care of our three wonderful sons through times of long absences for which am eternally grateful and I could not have wished for a better partner to travel through the journey of life with and there is only one thing left to say to Linda "Jag alsker dig".

John Taylor
7 July 2007